GAS TURBINE ENGINES
FOR PILOTS AND MECHANICS

by R.E. Birch

JEPPESEN®
Sanderson Training Products

© Jeppesen Sanderson, Inc., 2001
All Rights Reserved
55 Inverness Drive East, Englewood, CO 80112-5498
International Standard Book Number 0-88487-294-7

JS319025—000

For Jocelyne

TABLE OF CONTENTS

PREFACE TO THE SECOND EDITION

Technical books are assembled rather than written, and frequent reference to authoritative material has been necessary in the interests of accuracy. In cross-referencing information sources, a few imprecise or even contradictory presentations were encountered. In the latter case, decisions were made by the author, with accuracy of interpretation given top priority.

Fifty years of active flying in eleven countries provided the author with instruction. It has been impossible to identify individual sources since classroom notes and sketches used in this book's preparation were made in such diverse locations. The author wishes to thank and express appreciation to all who instructed so helpfully and patiently over those years.

The following pages attempt to cover the essential principles without involving minor topics. Chapters 20 and 21 supply a little information to "round off" the presentation and are for those who enjoy working with figures; others may safely skip them. However, the subject of performance, which marries engines to airframes, is important in its own right. It requires further study by all who would be professional pilots or mechanics.

R.E.Birch

INTRODUCTION

Aircraft gas turbine engines have been under active development for more than 60 years. Intensive efforts by highly competent engineers and technicians in various parts of the world have produced the smooth-running, reliable engines currently in use. An impressive amount of knowledge has been accumulated on the subject, enough to fill a library.

This book offers aspiring professional pilots and mechanics the fundamentals of the basic engine before studying in detail the engines they intend to fly or fix. Publications prepared by engine and propeller manufacturers will be needed for greater in-depth information.

In order to understand aircraft gas turbine engines, it is necessary to accept three simple concepts:

1.   Engine thrust is the reaction to the accelerations of gases passing through the engine, not the imagined "pushing" of the jet on the atmosphere.
2.   The burning of kerosene is only possible at very low speeds of airflow, nothing more than approximately 80 ft/sec at the burners.
3.   The speed of sound in air varies directly as the square root of the absolute temperature; the higher the temperature, the higher the speed of sound. High flow speeds require high temperatures so that local speed of sound is not exceeded. Allowing the flow speed to reach the speed of sound, Mach 1.0 (M 1.0) would create shock waves, resulting in pressure changes and turbulence increases.

Metrication has much to recommend it. In this book, the foot/pound/second (fps) system is used because the working pilot and mechanic encounter it daily.

Principles are the same worldwide; nomenclature may vary for similar things in varying places. Some flexibility may be necessary on the part of a reader. For example, turbine entry temperature (TET) in one area may be termed turbine inlet temperature (TIT) in another. Both refer to the same value.

Chapter 1

Brief History

The history of any subject can be surprising, and even when given only briefly, helps to put events into perspective. Before examining the internals of a gas turbine engine, we will briefly explore some of the past occurrences that have contributed to its development.

It has gone into print, erroneously, that jet engines were something completely new in the mid-1940s. Nothing could be further from the truth. The first recorded example of the application of jet reaction concerns the "Aeolipile" of Hero, the ancient Greek scientist. [Figure 1-1] A fire beneath a cauldron of boiling water

Figure 1-1. Hero's Aeolipile.

caused steam to pass into a metal sphere via vertical support tubes, and then to move out into the atmosphere through two right-angled nozzles. Reaction forces at the nozzle elbows resulted in the spinning of the sphere. Built in Alexandria, Egypt, in 120 B.C., the Aeolipile was used as a toy. There is no record of development being attempted.

Beginning about 1232 A.D., the Mongols used rockets in fireworks and in war. The people of China experimented with gunpowder as a rocket fuel in the same era.

About 1500 A.D., Leonardo da Vinci proposed not only a flying machine, a parachute, and an anemometer, but also a "turbine" to be placed in the rising hot air of a chimney. The rotary motion thus obtained was to be utilized by driving a spit for cooking purposes.

In the late 1500s, Simon Stevin, a Dutch mathematician, wrote a book on hydrostatics that included material on pressures in fluids. This helped lay the foundations upon which later calculations could be made.

Da Vinci's turbine sketch was more fully developed in 1648 by an English clergyman, John Wilkins, who placed a turbine, shaped like a Dutch-style windmill, in a chimney. A vertical shaft with gears at the lower end transmitted rotary motion for simple uses.

During the second half of the 17th century, an Italian mathematician, Evangelista Torricelli, worked on fluid research and invented the mercury barometer, which figures prominently in the calibration of modern engines. From the mercury barometer came the aneroid and aircraft altimeters.

Henri Pitot lived in France from 1695 to 1771. He was a famous hydraulic engineer whose major work was the construction of a water supply aqueduct for the city of Montpellier. The aqueduct included a stone arch more than a kilometer in length. An invention of his was the "pitot tube," which is used to measure fluid flow velocity. In addition to its use in all present-day aircraft as part of the airspeed indication system, the pitot principle is an important asset in evaluating gas turbine engine performance.

Most of the essential elements in today's gas turbine engines were included in a patent taken out in England in 1791 by John Barber. Modern knowledge shows that the design would not have worked. Nevertheless, it was a significant theoretical advance.

In the early 1800s, Giovanni Batista Venturi, an Italian physicist, studied the flow of fluids through reducing and expanding tubes. He is credited with the first development of what we now know as the venturi, an item of vital importance throughout gas turbine engines.

In 1872, Herr F. Stolze of Germany patented a machine incorporating a multi-stage axial flow compressor. The compressor delivered air via a heat exchanger to a multi-stage reaction turbine. The machine would not operate successfully because the turbine was not efficient enough to maintain rotation at temperatures acceptable to the materials of the time.

What was probably the first gas turbine engine capable of delivering work for commercial use operated in Paris in 1903. Compared with today's standards, efficiency was very low—only about 3%—but it worked.

In 1905, in Germany, Hans Holzworth advanced an original design of an explosion-type turbine. Together with associates, he continued experiments and development for the next 30 years.

In 1913, a Frenchman, Rene Lorin, took out a patent for the design of an aerothermodynamic duct (athodyd). Limitations imposed by materials, construction techniques, and the need for very high speed to initiate its functioning prevented its manufacture at that time. The principle is now applied in high-speed ramjet missiles and advanced turbo/ramjet engines. Figures 1-2 and 1-3 indicate the similarity in design of the 1913 concept and the functioning machines built 70 years later.

Frank Whittle's first jet patent was taken out in 1930 in England. Due to official disinterest, eleven years elapsed before the first flight of one of his engines.

By the mid-1930s, simultaneous independent research was going on in Italy, Germany, and Britain. Inevitably, there was an overlap of efforts and patents due to poor communication:

- The world's first aircraft jet flight was made on the 24th of August, 1939, in the German Heinkel HE 178.

- An Italian Caproni-Campini CC-2 flew in August 1940 using a form of jet motor. It was not a true gas turbine engine as we now know them, because the 3-stage compressor was driven by a piston engine.

- Frank Whittle's engine made its initial flight in England, May 1941, in the Gloster E 18/39.

In the United States, the first jet flight was made in October, 1942, using two General Electric 1-A engines developed from the Whittle design.

Fortunately for the Allied cause, the German High Command's belief that the war would be a short one made the High Command indifferent to scientific researchers' proposals for rapid development of rocket and jet applications. However, despite top-level apathy, by mid-1944, the Fieseler F 1.103 (V-1 flying bomb) was, without a pilot, using a form of jet motor to carry 850 kg of explosive from France to England and Belgium. Powered by an Argus 109-014 pulse jet unit of 660 lb of thrust, operating at 45 cycles per second, the machine had an extreme range of 160 nautical miles when consuming all 600 liters of fuel with which it was launched. [Figures 1-4 & 1-5]

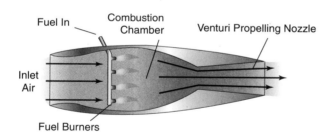

Figure 1-2. Lorin's 1913 patent.

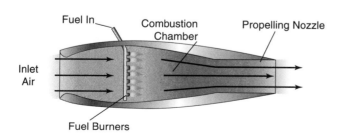

Figure 1-3. Modern ramjet principle.

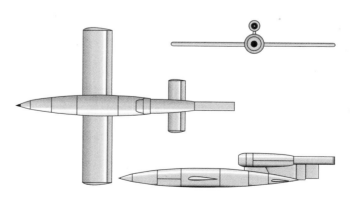

Figure 1-4. The V-1 flying bomb.

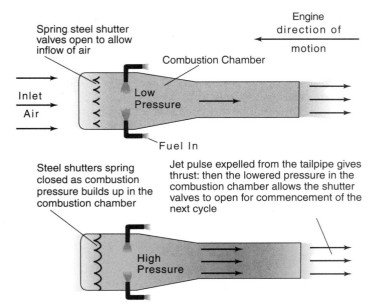

Figure 1-5. The pulse jet principle.

As fuel weight burned off, the V-1 had a top speed of about 430 knots. Interception was very difficult for even the fastest propeller-driven aircraft, and few jet interceptors were available.

In September, 1944, the liquid-fueled rocket known as the V-2 made its debut. The forerunner of space rock-

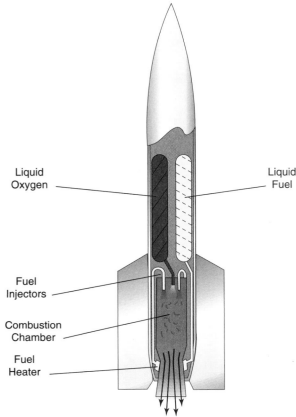

Figure 1-6.   The V-2.

ets, it routinely delivered 1,000-kg warheads over distances of up to 200 nautical miles. Forty-six feet tall and weighing 13 tons, it climbed to altitudes of some 50 nautical miles and achieved speeds of 2,600 knots. [Figure 1-6]

Four thousand V-2s were land launched in the seven months of their activity. Just before the end of hostilities, the first successful launch was carried out from a submerged submarine. It had been intended to use the V-2 from submarines, against American cities. The experience gained served as the basis for development of the Polaris and Poseidon systems. During the 1991 Desert Storm campaign, V-2s built in Iraq were known as "Scuds" and had their payload reduced by about 150 kg to allow additional fuel to be carried for increased range.

In September of 1944, Arado Ar 234 "Blitzs" began a series of high-altitude reconnaissance flights over the British Isles. The first of a number of German jet aircraft types, these twin-engined machines had a range of 1,340 nautical miles and impressive features such as ejection seats, automatic pilots, and pressurized cockpits.

Also entering active service at the same time were the highly advanced Messerschmitt ME 262 aircraft, powered by two Junkers Jumo 004B axial-flow gas turbine engines, each capable of producing 2,000 lb of thrust. [Figure 1-7]

Figure 1-7. The twin-jet ME 262.

More than 1,400 Messerschmitt ME 262s were built. Their axial-flow engines were very innovative, including ice protection, blade cooling, and variable-exhaust nozzles. At this time, rocket-propelled ME 163 "Komets" and jet-propelled HE 162 "Salamandas" were in production. All jet engines for these machines had short working lives, and were not reliable because good materials were not available.

The British Gloster "Meteor" first flew in 1943, and was powered by two centrifugal compressor turbo jets of Whittle design, each producing 1,700 lb of static thrust. Re-engined with more powerful engines, each with 3,500 lb thrust, a Meteor achieved a speed of 535 knots in 1945. [Figure 1-8]

Figure 1-8. The Gloster Meteor.

Meteors went into service with the RAF in July, 1944, shortly before the ME 262 took up squadron service with the Luftwaffe.

The impetus to aircraft and jet engine development did not cease with the end of World War II. Much effort and time have been expended on continual improvements. Initially, during the "Cold War," military needs pushed development, but more recently, commercial considerations have become primary. Basic principles of the very versatile gas turbine engine remain unchanged, and the following chapters should help to provide clarification.

Principles

All gas turbine engines used in aviation have a similar principle of functioning. A gas turbine engine (GTE) is a form of heat engine using air as the working fluid. As an "air breathing" engine, its use is limited to the earth's atmosphere, unlike the liquid-fueled rocket, which carries its own oxygen required for combustion and can therefore operate outside of the atmosphere. The straightforward functioning of a GTE is shown in figure 2-1.

Atmospheric air is taken into the engine and compressed in an axial flow or centrifugal compressor (sometimes by a sequenced combination of both). Following compression, the air is directed into one or more combustion chambers, where a fine spray of liquid fuel is added. This combustible mixture is ignited, sending hot gases onto one or more turbine wheels to cause their rotation. Some energy is extracted from the hot gases to drive the turbine(s), which in turn power the compressors so that the engine becomes "self sustaining." Hot gases are then expelled at high speed into the atmosphere via the exhaust jet pipe. The difference between the momentum of the exhaust gases and the momentum of the intake air provides the thrust in a "pure jet" engine. Only a small proportion of supplied air is involved in the actual combustion process. The remainder of the air provides cooling to acceptable values.

Both piston and jet aircraft engines work on air to accelerate it. The propeller of the piston type gives a low acceleration to a large mass of air, while the jet engine gives a large acceleration to a relatively small mass of air. For the latter to happen, increasing the velocity of the working air means increasing its energy; first by increasing the pressure energy, then by adding heat energy. Following some energy extraction by the turbine, residual energy is converted to kinetic energy in the high-velocity jet efflux.

Jet and four-stroke piston engines, having air as their working medium, both operate to similar working cycles. However, in the GTE, combustion takes place at a near-constant pressure. In the piston engine, combustion occurs at a constant volume.

Both GTEs and four-stroke piston engines work to a sequence of induction, compression, combustion, and exhaust. In the piston engine, the working cycle is intermittent, with a single component (the piston) being involved in all four actions. By contrast, the GTE has a continuous work cycle involving separate components (i.e. the compressor, combustor system, turbine, and exhaust).

In the GTE, the absence of reciprocating parts, combined with the continuous working cycle, produce a very smooth-running engine. Compared with a piston engine of any particular size, the GTE allows more energy to be released from a given quantity of fuel. On a pound-for-pound basis, the GTE is more efficient than the piston engine.

Because combustion in the GTE occurs at near-constant pressure with an increase in volume, the high peak

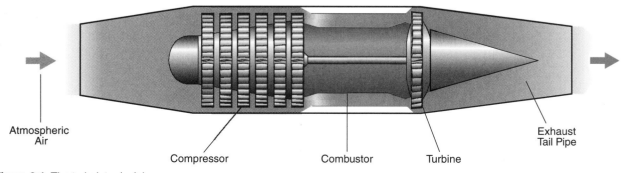

Figure 2-1. The turbojet principle.

Atmospheric Air

Compressor

Combustor

Turbine

Exhaust Tail Pipe

pressures of piston engines (1,000 psi or more) are avoided. It therefore becomes possible to use low-octane fuels and lightweight fabricated combustion chambers. To take advantage of their less-robust component requirements and to ensure long working lives, special materials are used in the GTE to withstand elevated temperatures.

The working cycle of an ideal GTE in its simplest form is shown in the left-hand PV (pressure – volume) diagram at the top of figure 2-2. The right-hand PV diagram shows the actual cycle resulting from inefficiencies in the intake compressor, combustor, turbine, and exhaust. [Figure 2-2]

Hatched areas to the left of the line 1 - 2 represent work done on the air during compression, and the areas between points 1 - 2 - 3 - 4 represent work produced by the engine during the cycle.

Point 1 shows air, at atmospheric pressure, which is compressed along line 1 - 2. In our engines, this takes place across the compressor.

From point 2 to 3, heat is added to the air by the introduction and combustion of fuel in the combustor at almost-constant pressure; the volume is increased. In the actual case, the small drop in pressure between 2 and 3 is due to necessary combustion-chamber construction practices.

From point 3 to 4, combustion products expand back to atmospheric pressure via the turbine and jet pipe. Some of the energy of the expanding gases is converted to mechanical energy in the turbine, and the remaining energy provides the propulsive jet when discharged into the atmosphere.

The sequence of events shown in the PV diagrams is known as the Brayton Cycle, named after George Brayton who did a great deal of theoretical analysis on steam engine performance in the United States in the 19th century. Sometimes referred to as Joule's Cycle, it concerns a thermodynamic cycle made up of two adiabatic and two isobaric changes taking place in alternate order. In GTEs, it is a continuous combustion cycle.

Throughout this book, reference is often made to the fact that raising the temperature of a gas will increase

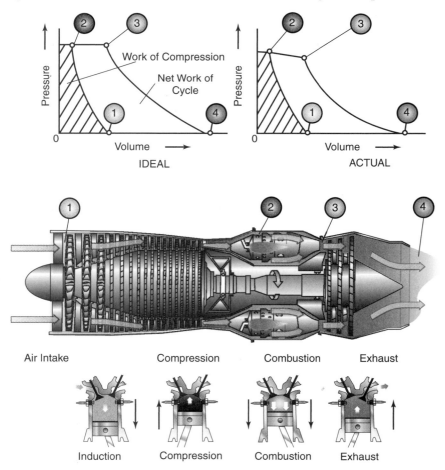

Figure 2-2. Comparison of work cycles.

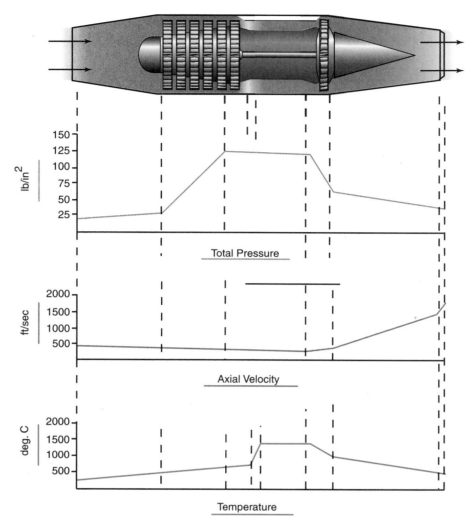

Figure 2-3. Pressure, velocity, and temperature variations.

its volume. When the action takes place within the finite limits of a GTE, increases in volume can be read as increases in gas velocity.

During the work cycle of a GTE, an air mass will take in and give out heat to produce changes in pressure, velocity, and temperature of that mass, as shown in figure 2-3. As changes occur, they are interrelated to conform with a combination of Boyle's and Charles' Laws; that is, the product of the pressure and volume of an air mass is proportional to the absolute temperature of the air at the stage, i.e. $PV \propto T$. Exact calculations relate to a perfect gas, which does not exist. However, the principles apply regardless of the means used to change the temperature; that is, whether during passage through the engine, gas temperature is increased by compression or combustion, or if further downstream in the engine, heat is extracted from the gases by the turbine. Because heat is a form of energy, variation in heat content of the gases is directly proportional to the work done on them, or taken from them, during passage through the engine. [Figure 2-3]

Changes occur in three main engine areas during the work cycle:

1. During compression, work is done on the air to increase its pressure and temperature, and to decrease its volume.

2. During combustion, fuel is added and burned. Temperature and volume of the gases increase while the pressure drops only slightly.

3. During expansion, the turbines extract energy from the gas stream to drive compressors and accessories. Decreases result in temperature and pressure.

As we have seen, mass airflow is continuous and volume changes are reflected directly as velocity changes.

Because the GTE is a heat engine, the higher the gas temperature, the greater both the expansion of gases

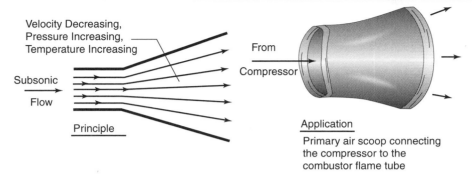

Figure 2-4. Divergent subsonic flow.

and the engine efficiency will be. However, combustion temperature must not be permitted to exceed the values acceptable to nozzle guide vane and turbine materials. Nevertheless, through use of air-cooled turbine blades and nozzle guide vanes, increases in temperature may be achieved to the point where environment temperature can be greater than the melting point of the materials. Cooling air, supplied through a large number of small holes on the component surfaces, forms extremely thin insulating layers over the components. Such cooling air should not be thought of as "cool" in terms of human comfort. The temperature of this air may well be several hundred degrees Celsius, but it is still cool relative to the nozzle guide vane/turbine environment.

Air passing through a GTE is subject to velocity and pressure changes to meet specific aerodynamic and energy needs. For example, during compression, a rise in air pressure is required, but not a rise in its velocity (recall the maximum airflow speed of 80 ft/sec for burning kerosene). After internal energy of the gas has been increased by combustive heating, an increase in its velocity is used to rotate the turbine. Subsequently, a higher velocity provides an increased thrust by adding to the momentum change.

The varying local requirements inside an engine give rise to complicated and demanding design considera-

tions. Necessary changes are brought about by altering the size and shape of the ducts through which gases pass.

Divergent passages convert kinetic (velocity) energy to pressure energy. [Figure 2-4] Convergent passages are used to change the pressure energy that is present in combustion gases into kinetic energy. [Figure 2-5]

Shapes such as these are used in the GTE where flow velocity is subsonic at the prevailing temperature. On the few occasions when supersonic flows are required, as in some exhaust-propelling nozzles, convergent-divergent ducts (venturis, figure 2-6) provide the maximum conversion into kinetic energy. An application of the convergent-divergent duct for subsonic/supersonic flow may be seen in figure 2-3. Note the propelling nozzle where there is a continuing pressure drop accompanied by a marked increase in axial velocity.

Remember that where Mach number is referred to in the GTE, it is the ratio of actual flow speed to the speed of sound in air at the local prevailing temperature (Mach No. = flow speed/speed of sound in air at local temperature). As a general rule, the speed of sound in liquids is higher than it is in air, and in solids it is much higher still.

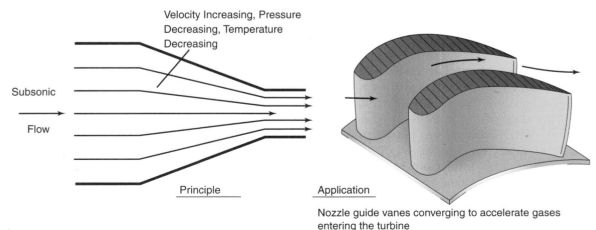

Figure 2-5. Convergent subsonic flow.

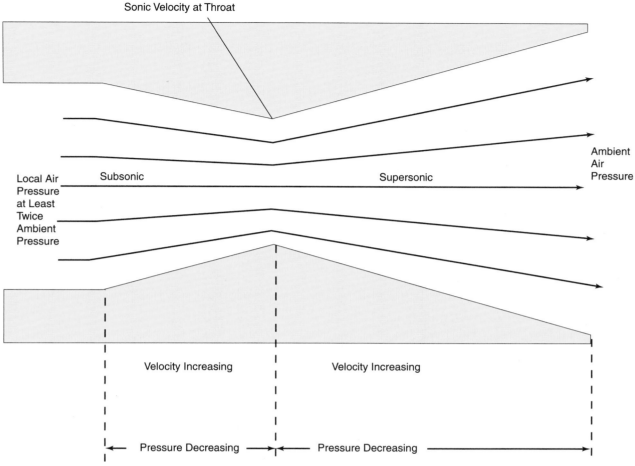

Figure 2-6. Supersonic flow achieved by a venturi.

The two lower graphs of figure 2-3 show that, even at elevated temperatures, the gas flow speed remains subsonic until the exhaust nozzle is reached.

Shaping of passages and nozzles is very important. The efficiency with which energy changes are brought about depends upon their good design. Turbulence loses efficiency, and eddies produce vibration with component failure.

Bernoulli's Theorem states that in the streamline flow of a perfect fluid (one without viscosity), "the sum of the energy of position (potential energy) plus the energy of motion (kinetic energy) plus the pressure energy will remain constant." In the case of the GTE, there is an insufficient change of height in the working fluid for potential energy variations to have any significant effect; hence, the sum of kinetic energy and pressure energy is considered constant. For a given mass of air transiting a GTE, kinetic energy that is lost results in pressure energy gained, and vice versa. In a venturi receiving subsonic flow, and having no big pressure variation across its entry and exit, Bernoulli's Theorem applies up to throat speeds of M 1.0 or slightly less. As M 1.0 is reached at the throat, a shock wave forms at almost 90 degrees to the throat surface and "chokes" the flow with a pressure rise downstream of the shock wave. [Figure 2-7]

The conservation of energy is only applicable for streamlined, non-turbulent flow of a perfect fluid. When flow speed at a venturi throat produces choking

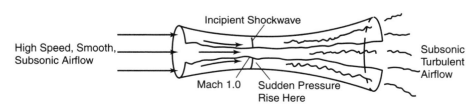

Figure 2-7. Subsonic venturi action.

shock waves, flow in the expanding section is turbulent, with pressure and velocity changes difficult or impossible to predict.

It is established that if a high pressure difference is maintained across a venturi receiving subsonic flow, which becomes sonic at the throat, the flow speed downstream of the throat will continue to accelerate and the pressure will drop in the diverging section. [Figure 2-6] However, if the flow presented to a convergent-divergent (CD) duct is already supersonic, the venturi effects are reversed. When approaching the throat, flow speed is reduced and pressure increases; and after, the throat speed increases and pressure drops. [Figure 2-8]

The divergent-convergent (DC) duct receiving supersonic flow has a similar reversal of subsonic venturi characteristics. In the diverging section, flow speed increases and pressure decreases, and in the converging section, speed decreases while pressure increases. [Figure 2-9]

Shock waves are in the order of 3/1000ths of a millimeter thick. At a shock wave, the gas pressure, temperature, and density increase suddenly and velocity decreases. In very advanced aircraft, the pressure increase behind shock waves is used to supplement the air pressure presented to the GTE. As would be imagined, extremely careful design is required. The higher pressure downstream of a shock wave cannot move forward through the wave to lower pressure upstream. The history of research at transonic speeds, for airframes and engines, has been unsatisfactory. Shock wave choking of experimental equipment, up to and including large wind tunnels, has caused much uncertainty. In the flow speed range of approximately M 0.85 to M 1.10, empirical results achieved in practice have tended to precede theoretical concept developments.

So, not only is the shaping of passages and nozzles important, but also the speed of flow through those components is a significant influence upon results.

ENGINE TYPES

The actual flow path through a GTE varies according to requirements. The straight-through flow, as in figure 2-1, is the basic design, providing a small frontal area combined with a suitability for bypass arrangements.

Various forms of GTE have evolved as different requirements have been met. Some of the principles are shown in figures 2-10 to 2-16, which follow.

The bypass principle is attractive, as it improves both propulsive efficiency and specific fuel consumption. At its simplest, air is taken in at the front of the engine and given a low compression. Part of that air is then bypassed around the combustion areas and ejected either as a separate flow or mixed with the final jet efflux. [Figure 2-10]

The bypass ratio is the ratio of air bypassing the combustion zone to the amount of air entering that zone. In the early days of low bypass ratios, 1 : 1 was the norm, whereas later GTEs use ratios of 8 : 1 or higher as the search for greater efficiency and lower fuel consump-

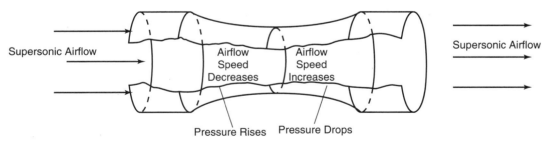

Figure 2-8. Supersonic flow through a CD duct.

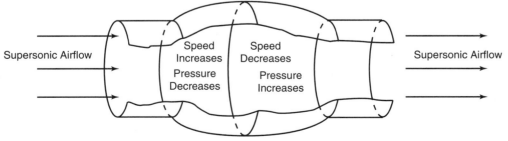

Figure 2-9. Supersonic flow through a DC duct.

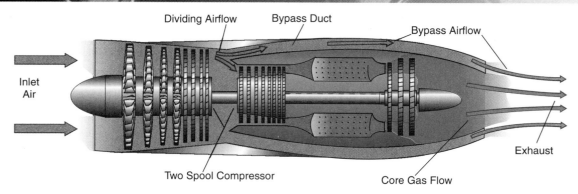

Figure 2-10. The bypass principle.

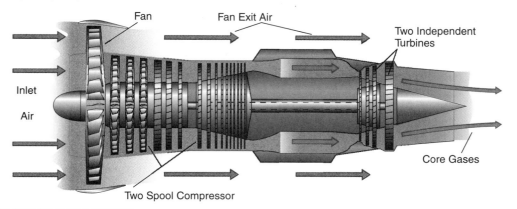

Figure 2-11. The front fan bypass principle.

tion continues. While low-bypass engines usually mix hot and cold streams before the engine exit, it is common for higher-bypass engines to exhaust in separate hot and cold streams.

In the front fan engine, the fan forms the first stage of the low-pressure compressor to which it is attached, and the low pressure (LP) turbine drives the LP compressor, including the fan. Bypass air from the fan may be discharged around the engine, or carried in ducts for the full length of the engine, before being exhausted.

The latter gives rise to the terms "ducted bypass" and "ducted fan." [Figure 2-11]

Although aft fans have been produced and put into service, they are now seldom used. This is because of practical difficulties presented by having the outer sections of the fan blades exposed to cold air, while the inner part forms the turbine blading in hot gases. Thermal stresses, expansion, and sealing problems make the concept impractical, despite initial apparent advantages of design simplicity. [Figure 2-12]

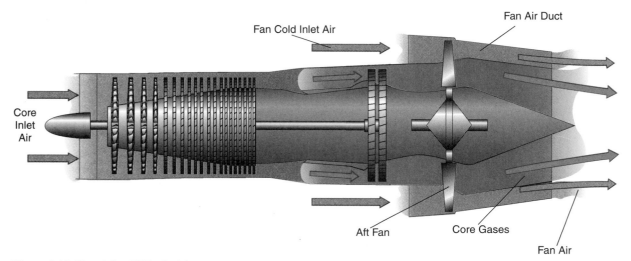

Figure 2-12. The aft fan GTE principle.

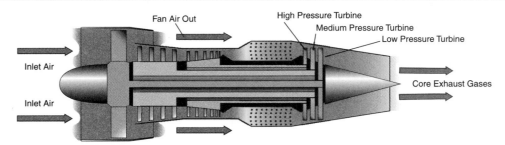

Figure 2-13. The three-spool front fan principle.

A variation of the front fan has a three-spool engine, with the fan being driven at optimum aerodynamic speed by its own turbine. [Figure 2-13]

The major departure of the shaft engine from other GTEs is its conversion of gas energy into mechanical energy to drive a shaft. The shaft may be used to drive a propeller, a helicopter rotor, or any form of industrial application such as a ship's propulsive screw or a power house's electrical generator.

After the high pressure turbine has taken a large proportion of gas power to drive the compressor, most of the remaining stream energy is absorbed by additional turbine stages to power the shaft. Only a residual amount of energy is available for jet thrust at the tailpipe. The fixed-wing turboprop application is of most consequence here.

There are three principal types of turboprop:

1. The directly connected turboprop

2. The compound compressor turboprop

3. The free turbine turboprop

The directly connected turboprop, shown in figure 2-14, would cause cranking problems during engine start if it was not fitted with a propeller having special "ground fine pitch" capabilities. A piston engine starter

motor is required to provide cranking only until the engine fires. The GTE starter must continue to give cranking torque after light up until the engine reaches self-sustaining speed. If the propeller was not capable of going below the flight fine pitch setting, it would produce ever-increasing drag as the engine r.p.m. rose. To provide the necessary torque, the GTE starter would be bulky and heavy; and most starter systems are redundant once the engine is at self-sustaining speed. The alternative used in the directly connected turboprop is to give the propeller a "ground fine pitch" setting, something in the order of zero to six degrees of blade angle when needed.

Usually a landing gear "squat switch" opens an electric circuit on takeoff. A flight fine pitch lock is then positioned to prevent blade angles from being below flight fine while airborne. On landing, the squat switch closes the electric circuit, withdraws the flight fine pitch lock, and allows the propeller blades to go into ground fine. The "disking" provided by the propeller, which is comparable to presenting a metal disk at 90 degrees to the airflow, provides a useful retarding action to the aircraft when it is automatically selected on landing. An aircraft with this feature responds in a similar fashion to one using reverse thrust early in a landing roll. The propeller "constant speeds" between ground fine and flight fine for taxiing and ground operations.

The directly connected turboprop has the propeller pitch and engine fuel controls interconnected, and an accelerator control is incorporated in the constant speed

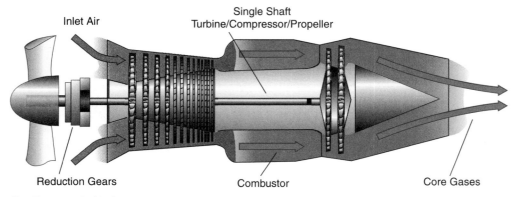

Figure 2-14. The directly connected turboprop.

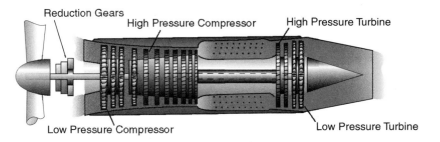

Reduction Gears
High Pressure Compressor   High Pressure Turbine
Low Pressure Compressor   Low Pressure Turbine

Figure 2-15. A compound compressor turboprop.

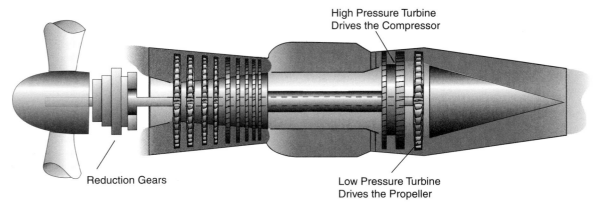

High Pressure Turbine
Drives the Compressor

Reduction Gears

Low Pressure Turbine
Drives the Propeller

Figure 2-16. A free turbine turboprop.

unit to ensure a correct relationship between propeller r.p.m. and the selected engine fuel flow. Without these features, a coarse propeller setting combined with a large throttle opening could result in the propeller over-loading the engine and cause compressor blade stall and engine overheating.

Compound compressor (figure 2-15) and free turbine (figure 2-16) turboprops do not require ground fine pitch capability as their propellers are not mechanically connected to the starters during cranking. However, propellers having reverse-thrust range are fitted to many turboprop aircraft.

Various propeller features are provided to protect air-craft in the event of engine power or operating system malfunction on takeoff or in flight. Fortunately, system failures are rare and becoming more so; but Murphy is always nearby.

The handling of all possible propeller malfunctions for any particular turboprop system must be completely understood. Catastrophic windmill drag and/or excessive r.p.m. can quickly follow a malfunction at higher airspeeds, including cruise.

There will be no time to look it up in a book.

Finally, in this outline of principles, figure 2-17 is the simplest of graphs that illustrates the most important item for a piston engine pilot converting to GTEs.

Significant thrust is only produced by a GTE when operating at or beyond about 80% of its r.p.m. range.

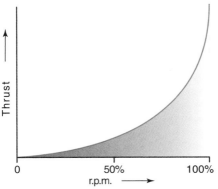

Thrust

0   50%   100%
r.p.m. ⟶

Figure 2-17. GTE thrust vs. r.p.m.

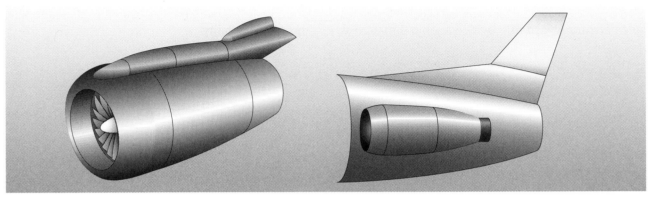

Chapter 3

Air Intakes

Figure 3-1. Pitot-type air intakes.

Having established the basic principles connected with the GTE, we move to examine major sections of typical engines, commencing at the front and working aft.

An engine air intake is required to deliver the amount of air necessary for all operating conditions and must do so while producing the least possible energy losses. For the compressor to function satisfactorily, intake air must be presented to it at a single pressure and spread uniformly across the whole area of the inlet.

The "pitot-type" intake is ideal for a turbojet aircraft operating at subsonic or low supersonic speeds. It has a full round intake, which is presented to the airflow at 90 degrees. [Figure 3-1]

The ram air intake effect due to aircraft forward speed is maximized while losses due to attitude changes are minimized. At transonic aircraft speed, losses due to shock waves around intake lips may cause efficiency to be lowered. For this reason, pitot-type intakes are limited to speeds below about M 1.5.

Pitot-type intakes are satisfactory for engines in pods mounted either at the wing or tail of the aircraft. They are also suitable for engines buried in the aircraft wing but may need variation from the full round shape for airframe structural reasons.

Use of a pitot-type intake in the nose of a single-engine aircraft can result in an unsatisfactorily long duct ahead of the compressor inlet. To avoid using a long tunnel duct, divided-type intakes in the leading edges of wing roots are often adopted.

This configuration may produce an interfered airflow when the aircraft yaws, thus giving an irregular air supply to the compressor. A similar yaw interference is caused if the aircraft is fitted with intakes that are located on each side of the front section of the fuselage. [Figure 3-2]

As mentioned earlier, at transonic and supersonic aircraft speeds, some engines enhance the compression of

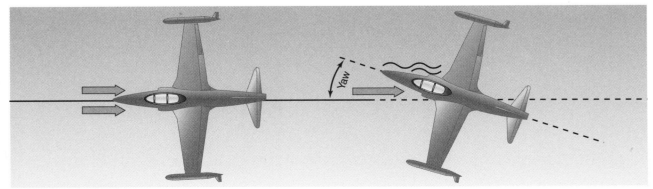

Figure 3-2. Divided-type intakes.

working air. They do this by positioning intake shock waves in such a way that the pressure rise behind the wave adds to the compressor inlet pressure. To control this increase, a "spike," which can be adjusted fore and aft relative to the intake, is used to position the shock wave coming from its tip.

Greater aircraft speeds may raise the intake compression beyond acceptable limits unless special design features are introduced to provide variable throat areas; spilling of excess air may be required. Maximum airflow speed for the burning of kerosene remains a limitation. At such higher flight speeds, airflow velocity between intake entry and compressor entry is adjusted by spilling part of the airflow. Published figures for the Concorde give the order of numbers: when aircraft cruise speed is M 2.02, compressor intake air is presented at about M 0.7 to M 0.8. Aircraft featuring prominent "square" intakes can be expected to have this spill capability.

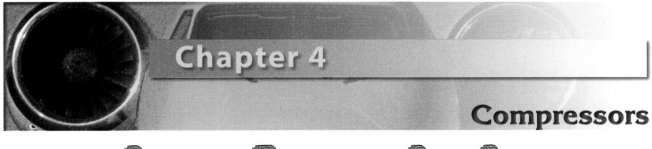

Single Entry

Double Entry

Two Stage

Figure 4-1   **Centrifugal impellers.**

The custom has developed in aviation for a turbine/shaft/compressor assembly that rotates as a single unit to be referred to as a "spool." From this, it is customary to refer to an engine at its higher r.p.m. as being "spooled up." Gas turbine engines (GTEs) produce the major part of their thrust in the high r.p.m. range, thus an "unspooled" engine may be at 50% of its permitted r.p.m. but only developing a small percentage of its maximum thrust. On approach for landing in heavier aircraft, safety requires engines to be "spooled up" to allow for an immediate aircraft response to throttle movements.

Two types of compressors are used in GTEs:

1. Centrifugal flow compressors

2. Axial flow compressors

Normally one or the other is used, and the axial flow is common, although sometimes air is delivered to combustors by a combination of both types. "Straight through" air passage for the length of the engine can be considered the usual with "reverse flow" permitting a reduction of engine length, making it more compact for special applications in some helicopters and turbo-props.

Centrifugal flow types may feature single- or two-stage impellers, and some single units may be double sided. [Figure 4-1] An impeller accelerates air while compressing it, and a diffuser continues the pressure build-up while reducing airflow velocity.

Multistage axial compressors use alternate rows of rotating and static blades. A stage comprises one row of rotating blades plus the next downstream row of stator blades. Axial compressors of 13 stages or more are in operation. Alternate cycles of acceleration and deceleration are carried out until the required pressure rise is achieved. The following graphs show pressure and velocity variations in the operation of centrifugal and axial types. [Figure 4-2]

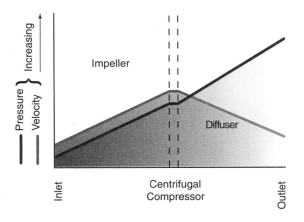

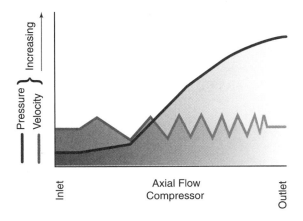

Figure 4-2. Pressure and velocity variations.

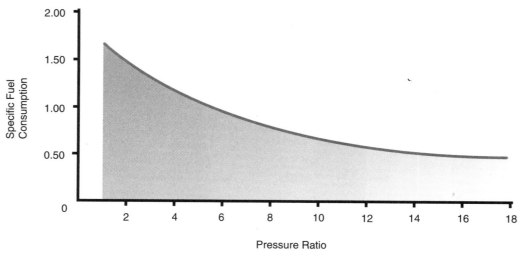

Figure 4-3. Decreasing fuel consumption.

A common feature of both types of compressors is that specific fuel consumption of the engine decreases as the compression ratio rises. Higher compression ratios are obtainable by the axial compressor, hence its greater appeal. [Figure 4-3]

Most early jet engines used centrifugal compressors that were easily derived from existing supercharger compressors from big piston engines. In addition to being robust, centrifugal units have the advantage of being relatively simple to manufacture. They are often used in smaller engines to combine simplicity with ruggedness that is needed to cope with diverse field conditions.

Rotation of the centrifugal impeller induces airflow into its center. The air is given radial motion by centrifugal action, and the air pressure rises. Accelerated compressed air from the impeller passes into a ring of diverging diffuser blades, which give direction to the air while decelerating it to produce a further pressure

rise. Processed air is collected in the compressor manifold for onward passage to the burner cans. [Figure 4-4]

Rapid rotation gives impeller tip speeds up to about 1,600 ft/sec. This produces the high air velocity necessary for the efficient conversion of velocity to pressure with smooth airflow.

As shown in the left-hand graph of figure 4-2, about half of the total pressure rise of a centrifugal compressor is produced in the impeller and half in the diffuser. Very small clearances are maintained between the rotating impeller and its stationary case to reduce air leakage. Clearances for the impeller/diffuser assemblies must be precise in order to prevent vibration.

Diffusers may be incorporated as integral parts of the compressor manifold or may be separately attached assemblies. In all types, diffusion is achieved by curved vanes tangential to the impeller.

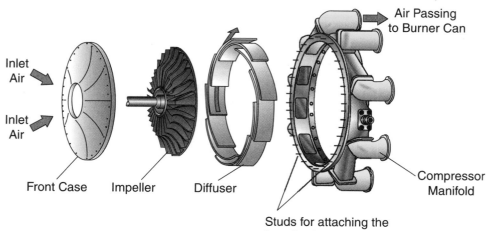

Inlet Air

Inlet Air

Air Passing to Burner Can

Front Case   Impeller   Diffuser

Compressor Manifold

Studs for attaching the impeller front case to the compressor manifold.

Figure 4-4. Centrifugal compressor manifold.

Fixed swirl vanes are often provided to direct intake air onto the eye of the impeller at the best angle for efficiency. Some impeller vanes have the central parts of their leading edges curved forward in the direction of rotation. Acting in unison with swirl vanes, these curved parts smooth the airflow into the impeller. Curved leading edge parts may be integral to impeller vanes or may be separate pieces; the latter allow more accurate machining.

Impeller disks are forgings with integral radial vanes on one or both sides. These radial vanes, which may be straight for ease of manufacture, form divergent passages when mated with the compressor cases.

When in operation, axial compressors induce an inflow of air and pass it down their length with alternate accelerations and decelerations. Rotating blades impart velocity to the air in each stage and the following stator blades convert velocity to pressure energy as shown in the right-hand graph of figure 4-2. The final stator blades direct air to the combustors in a straight axial flow. As pressure increases along the length of the axial compressor, temperature also rises, as illustrated in Chapter 2, figure 2-3.

Although sensitive to foreign object damage (FOD), axial flow compressors are preferred because of their ability to provide the necessary high compression ratios. As mass airflow is a major factor in producing thrust, an axial flow engine will provide more thrust than the centrifugal counterpart of a similar frontal area. Additionally, the manufacturer may add extra blades to an axial compressor in subsequent development to increase thrust by increasing pressure ratio. Because aircraft have become so expensive, this option is very attractive to operators.

As compression ratios increase, the difficulty of efficient operation over the entire engine r.p.m. range also increases. To achieve the best results at high r.p.m., the ratio of compressor intake area to its discharge area needs to be large. Consequently, as r.p.m. decreases when the throttle is retarded, the high intake/discharge areas ratio becomes too great. To meet the reduced requirement for intake mass airflow, the velocity of entering air is reduced until it is too slow to match the blade r.p.m. As angles of attack of the blades increase, flow over the airfoil-shaped blades breaks down, resulting in the stalling of the front stage blades. [Figure 4-5]

When high pressure ratios are required in a single spool compressor, the possibility of stalling is reduced by the use of spill valves, which automatically remove and dump some air from the compressor mid-section. This

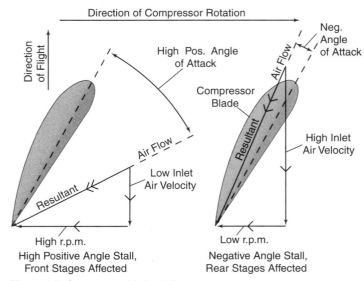

Figure 4-5. Compressor blade stalls.

method reduces the axial velocity through the preceding stages but wastes energy. A preferred, more economic method uses automatic, variably angled stator blades in the compressor front stages. Those automatically variable stator blades adjust their angular settings relative to the longitudinal axis as the pressure ratios and r.p.m. vary; good directional feed of air to the following rotor blades is assured.

The tendency for blade stalling due to an increase in pressure ratio between stages is reduced by having only a small increase across each stage. Normally, inlet to outlet pressure ratios are between 1 : 1 and 1 : 2. It should be noted that, although the ratio increase across each stage is small, the final pressure can be quite high because of the number of stages. Carefully controlled air velocities and straight-through flow contribute to high efficiency with minimum energy losses. Because of varying stage airflow requirements, designing efficient compressors calls for carefully matching every stage with the characteristics of its neighbors. The matching process is not too difficult for one set of conditions, but it does become very complex when considering the whole range of operating circumstances to which an aircraft might be exposed.

A single-spool axial compressor has one rotating assembly with as many stages as required for pressure rise. Although an engine with a twin-spool compressor can put all its air through the turbine as a pure jet, the configuration generally leads to a bypass arrangement like the single spool engine.

Further development of the bypass principle led to the introduction of fan engines in which inner sections of fans form the first row of low-pressure (LP) compressor blades, while outer sections of fan blades accelerate the bypass air. The fan is part of the LP compressor with which it rotates, and the whole is driven by the LP turbine. The front fan bypass principle is illustrated in Chapter 2, figure 2-11. A variation of the front fan, the three-spool engine with the fan being driven at optimum aerodynamic speed by its own turbine, is illustrated in Chapter 2, figure 2-13. The high bypass turbo fan engine is a development of earlier fan engines. A large-diameter fan is driven by its own dedicated turbine at optimum speed. Inner sections of fan blades pass air into the LP compressor, while the much bigger outer sections accelerate large quantities of bypass air in a manner similar to a conventional propeller.

For best performance, bypass flow pressure needs to be approximately 1.6 times the ambient air pressure. This is achieved by having fan tip speeds as high as 1,500 ft/sec. However, by using a dedicated turbine for the fan alone, it can operate closer to its aerodynamic best; variable angle-of-attack blades provide further improvement. Although use of reduction gearing in the fan drive is a complication, it is considered acceptable. Engine weight and overall mechanical complexity are reduced by the combination of fan and compressor. Improvements result without the use of inlet guide vanes. Bypass and fan engines provide high sub-sonic speeds for airline operations. Accelerations for large masses of air are, in principle, similar for both turboprops and fans. While turboprops are sometimes referred to as being extensions of large fan engines, chronologically, the turboprop preceded the fan.

The words "surge" and "stall" of an axial compressor mean different things to different people. To some, a surge is blade stalling over a few stages, while stalling amounts to total breakdown of airflow through the whole compressor. To other people, the word meanings are reversed. It probably matters little which is used, provided there is no breakdown in communication. Pilots seem to lean to the first definition, which is the one used here.

A disruption of airflow over the blades due to a change in angle of attack, i.e. blade stall, can be brought on in one of two ways. The first concerns the high angle of attack or positive angle stall, which is much like the aerodynamic stall of the airplane itself. This may occur in a compressor having a low inlet velocity combined with high engine r.p.m., and it affects the front stages of the compressor.

The second is the low angle of attack or negative angle stall. This is comparable to inverting an airplane, then pushing its nose above the horizon to stall the wings while still inverted. Such a stalling of compressor blades may occur when high inlet air velocity is combined with low engine r.p.m.; rear compressor blades will be affected (see Figure 4-5).

A surge involving a few compressor stages will be accompanied by a low rumble, discernable in the cockpit. A complete compressor stall produces a violent explosion noise that leaves no one in doubt. This happens when the stalling of all stages reduces the compressor pressure below combustor pressure. A long tongue of flame shoots forward from the air intake accompanied by a loud bang and loss of thrust. Explosive compressor stalls are startling for all on board; however, engine damage is not common.

A compressor stall reduces airflow through the engine and the fuel control unit reduces the fuel flow. This decreases back pressure on the compressor and allows an increase in airflow, which clears the stall condition. The fuel control unit then restores the fuel flow, and the compressor back pressure rises again. If this back pressure becomes too great, the stall will occur again, and the cycle repeats. Most compressor stalls take place during engine acceleration or at high altitude. A strong crosswind on takeoff adds to the possibility of a stall. However, design improvements have almost eliminated the phenomenon. Variable inlet guide vanes, variable stator blades, and two-spool compressors rotating at different speeds help alleviate the problem. In addition, improved automatic fuel control units compensate for rapidly changing conditions.

To clear the most common compressor stalls, engine r.p.m. and fuel flow should be reduced, if at all practicable, by retarding throttles.

The importance of throttle closing in flight may not be evident. In normal flight of piston-engined aircraft, the only time a throttle will be fully closed is just before touchdown. "Balanced power" restrictions on the combination of manifold pressure and engine r.p.m. of large piston-engined aircraft mean that the throttle is partly open throughout flight. The situation is very different in a turbine-powered aircraft.

Newer aircraft, which feature computers and a coupled autopilot, do the whole job with maximum efficiency. Older turbine aircraft still require a "hands on" descent. Although variations will be required by some operators and traffic control authorities, or by particular engine and airframe combinations, turbine engine aircraft easily carry out the entire descent with throttles fully retarded. Engines idle smoothly, there is little risk of the "light going out," and residual thrust is reduced to something between zero and 1,000 lb. (However, some

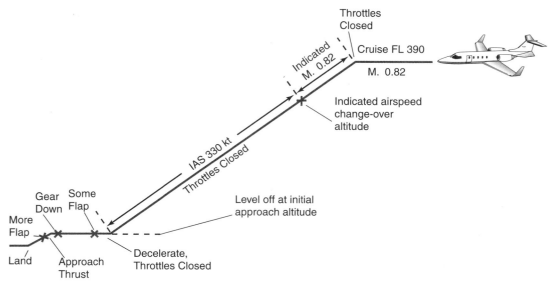

Figure 4-6. Possible descent profile.

older engines require monitoring to maintain tailpipe temperature above a certain minimum level.) [Figure 4-6]

The technique calls for maintaining Mach number, about M 0.82, when entering descent by slowly closing the throttles fully and holding the Mach number by varying the rate of descent. At "change over" altitude, aircraft forward speed is controlled by IAS rather than Mach number, and is held constant thereafter, as in figure 4-6. When traffic or established control restrictions do not apply, the high IAS can be held until 1,500 ft. above the destination runway. Then, while maintaining a constant altitude, airspeed is allowed to bleed off until flap and gear extension speeds are reached. With their extension, throttles are opened as required for final approach. Nothing is proved by all of this, but it gives some satisfaction to close the throttles above 30,000 ft. and not need to touch them, or to use speed brakes, until on long final. A rough rule of thumb for commencing descent is 3 x FL, i.e. at FL 330, commence descent at 99 DME.

Modifications to the basic technique may be brought on by head or tail winds, cabin pressurization needs, en route weather, traffic, and descent clearances; they are of no further interest at this time.

The message is that full closing of GTE throttles in the air can be quite routine and the engines remain running smoothly.

Because of high centrifugal loads, axial compressor rotor blades must be securely attached to central drum disks, which are themselves bolted or welded together. Two methods are shown in figure 4-7. Rotor blades are machined to airfoil shapes with a high degree of accuracy. They are given a "twist" to provide a pressure gra-

dient along the span of each blade, thereby producing a uniform velocity of axial airflow. Twisting the blades produces equal angles of attack over the blade span in the same way as twisting does in normal propeller blades.

Axial compressor stator vanes are also of airfoil design; they may be attached to the outer case directly as single units, or they may be assembled in vane retaining rings, which are then attached to the case in segments. Longer stator vanes may tend to vibrate, which is overcome by fitting shrouds to the vane ends.

Materials used in aviation engine manufacture are those having the best combination of heat resistance, high strength, and low weight. Aluminum is used at the front of the compressor casing. Further aft, steel alloys are used because working temperatures increase.

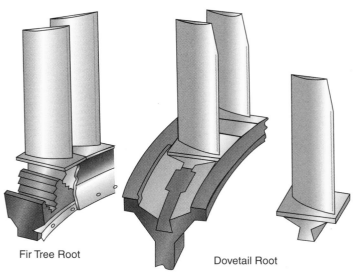

Fir Tree Root   Dovetail Root

Figure 4-7. Blade attachment.

Nickel-based alloys suit compressor areas having the highest temperatures, however, titanium is becoming more favored for construction in critical areas. This case, which carries rows of stator vanes, may be assembled around the rotor by joining two halves. Alternatively, it may be made up of a number of short cylinders bolted together.

Steel or nickel alloys are materials most used for stator vanes, but titanium is used for compressor rotor blades, disks, and drums that carry high centrifugal loads when working. Large-diameter fan blades are also made of titanium to combine low weight with high strength.

Rotating assemblies are carried on self-aligning shafts mounted in bearings that are located in compressor casings. In all rotating parts of a GTE, balance is of utmost importance. Special machines are used to ensure that the correct degree of balance is achieved.

Chapter 5

Combustors

The combustion chamber, whether it's a single unit or made up of several "cans," has the difficult task of ensuring stable and efficient combustion over the full range of possible conditions. It must provide satisfactory operation over all variations of r.p.m., altitude, attitude, air pressure and temperature, TAS, and "g" loading.

Combustion chambers will be one of three main types:

1. Can

2. Annular

3. Can-annular

In each, less than one-third of the air entering the chamber takes part in the initial combustion process. The air/fuel ratio, by weight, would be anything from 40 : 1 to perhaps 140 : 1, and kerosene burns best at a ratio of about 15 : 1. Also, kerosene will not burn if airflow speed exceeds 80 ft./sec. Compressed air approaches the combustor at velocities of up to 500 ft./sec. Obviously, both the quantity and speed of air presented for combustion must be reduced. The front section of combustors is designed to divide airflow and to slow the part that is to mix with the atomized fuel.

Ignition of the air/fuel mixture is provided by the electric spark of an igniter plug similar in design and function to a reciprocating engine's spark plug. Once ignited, the flame is self-sustaining, if stable conditions remain. However, if it is in the starting cycle, the engine must continue to be cranked by the starter until r.p.m. build up to such a value that engine operation also becomes self-sustaining.

The limited amount of air taking part in the combustion process is known as "primary air;" amounting to approximately 20% of the total air entering the burner. It passes via the snout, swirl vanes, and perforated flare to the actual combustion zone. The ignited swirling mixture combines with a further 20% of the total air that enters by way of holes in the combustor walls. Fuel combustion is thereby completed and the remaining secondary air is progressively added for further cooling.

Air temperature from the compressor ranges from 200° C to 550° C, and rises in the combustion chamber to a range of 600 to 1650 C degrees. Temperature limits are decided by nozzle guide vane and turbine materials. At the flame itself, the gas temperature can be as high as 2,200° C. To avoid incomplete combustion, all burning must be completed before the addition of secondary cooling air.

There are no particular rules about the use of cans as combustors. The type is most often used in conjunction with centrifugal compressors. When combustion is complete, hot gas streams converge just upstream of the entry to the nozzle guide vanes, which direct that flow onto the high-pressure (HP) turbine. [Figure 5-1]

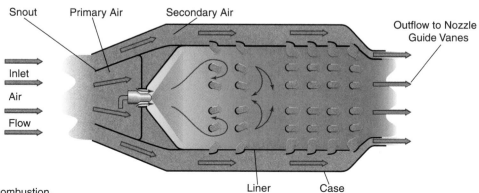

Figure 5-1. Can combustion.

Advantages for the can are:

1. Service life is very good.

2. Individual cans may be removed for inspection or replacement without disturbing an installed engine.

3. Compared with an annular-type combustion chamber, each can has a smaller diameter and thus has improved structural strength combined with light weight.

An annular combustion chamber is well suited for use with an axial flow compressor. The annular chamber is fitted around the outside of the compressor driveshaft housing and is composed of inner and outer shrouds with baffles forming the fuel burners. Fuel is introduced through a number of nozzles that are located in the upstream end of the combustor. Secondary cooling air passes through holes in the baffles to provide a cooling air blanket on both sides of the liner. The air also centers the combustion flame so it does not contact the liner. [Figure 5-2]

Compared with other GTE components, all combustor parts require more frequent inspections and replacement. Some engines that employ annular combustion chambers need to be removed from the aircraft and partially dismantled to carry out these operations.

In terms of actual efficiency, the annular chamber is very good. Within the limited space available, this configuration provides a near-optimum mixture of fuel and air while permitting relatively simple construction. When resisting distortions due to heat, adequate cooling is achieved with a 15% reduction of cooling air. Increased combustion efficiency eliminates the production of poisonous carbon monoxide (CO) but adds to the amount of carbon dioxide (CO_2) produced. In the short term, this is an advantage, although as mentioned

later, adding CO_2 to the atmosphere has become increasingly problematic.

Many large turbojet and turbofan engines make use of the can-annular type of combustion chamber. [Figure 5-3]

Individual cans are placed side by side to form a circle inside an annular chamber. These cans are essentially separate combustion chambers, and have rings of perforations in the walls to admit cooling air. Around the forward end of each can are about half a dozen fuel nozzles. Some designs have a perforated tube running down the center of each can. Its purpose is to provide extra air for combustion and cooling. The shape provides more burning per linear inch of can.

The can-annular combustion chamber combines the best features of both the can and annular designs while eliminating some of their disadvantages. Either a removable or a telescopic shroud covers the entire burner assembly. Cans are easily accessible for removal without taking the engine from the aircraft.

The design provides an even temperature distribution at the HP turbine inlet, minimizing the risk of hot spots if a fuel nozzle should become blocked. Also, the short burner length prevents excessive pressure drop between the compressor and the flame area.

Pollution of the atmosphere has become an important issue all over the world. In any combustion process, smoke indicates incomplete burning. Unburned carbon particles that are visible as smoke imply an incomplete combustion and indicate the presence of additional greenhouse gases. So-called "smokeless burners" have been developed by aero engine manufacturers. However, their improvement in performance efficiency is actually minimal, although they do contribute to

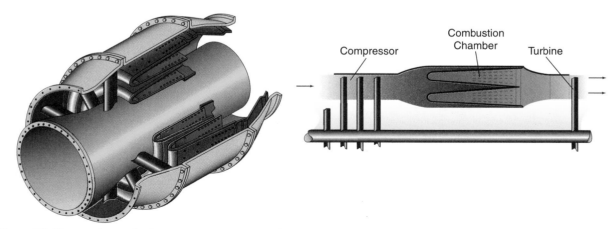

Figure 5-2. The annular combustor.

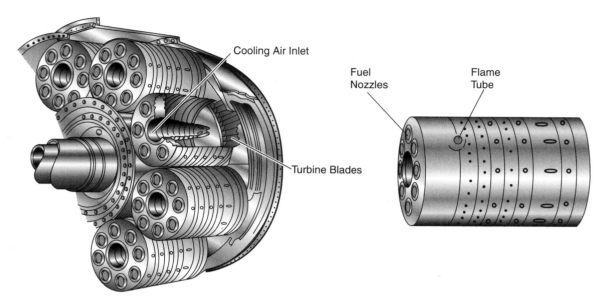

Figure 5-3. Can-annular construction.

reductions in aesthetic complaints from communities living around airports.

In the 1970s, it was possible to fly over France and Germany into Scandinavia with clear blue skies, while high above was an increasing criss-cross of contrails from exercizing NATO aircraft. Returning by the same route a few hours later, the contrails could be seen to have merged into a continuous sheet of cirrus cloud, which thickened during the day. There was even a Swiss area that complained bitterly and demanded compensation because tourists were staying away from what had previously been a sunny place in the Alps.

During World War I, it was noticed that heavy, wet weather followed big artillery barrages, which put a multitude of condensation nuclei into the atmosphere. From this fact came the meteorological term "front."

Smoking factory chimneys and all forms of combustion create greenhouse gases. One apparent result of all these gasses is the hole in the ozone layer, larger than Europe, which exists in the Southern Hemisphere. The atmosphere's ability to screen the sun's ultraviolet (UV) radiation is reduced in Australia due to this hole. Cancer causing melanomas are becoming much more common.

During the summer, daily levels of UV are broadcast on television. This is just a foretaste of what will happen to the whole planet unless the production of greenhouse gases is reduced.

Conventional GTEs produce CO, CO_2, nitrous oxide (N_2O), and traces of other noxious gases in their combustion chambers. The European Commission (EC), United States, and Japan have set commendable targets for reducing these gases. Target figures providing up to 80% reduction have been set for engines of the future.

Chapter 6

Turbines

The turbine has the important task of driving the compressor and engine accessories. It uses a considerable amount of energy in doing so. In fact, about 75% of the total energy in the hot gas stream is required for this purpose. Design and manufacture excellence are essential. High temperatures in the nozzle guide vane/high-pressure turbine area are critical in determining engine life. Alert monitoring of temperatures is a major activity of the cockpit crew.

In simpler, pure jets, the turbine powers a single compressor. With axial-flow engines, greater efficiency is achieved by using low- and high-pressure compressors, each operating at its own optimum speed. Gearing for different speeds would be complex. By careful design, two turbines can operate independently of each other and provide, via concentric shafts, the required r.p.m. to each compressor section.

In the same way as we speak of a stage in the compressor, we can refer to a stage in the turbine. However, in the turbine, a stage is a row of static vanes plus the following turbine row.

Metal disks are attached to power-transmitting shafts and carry the turbine blades on their outer edges. Hot gases from the combustor travel through the nozzle guide vanes to impinge upon the blades and produce turbine rotation. Disks have cooling air from the compressor supplied through holes near the disk center. The cooling air flows radially across the disk face toward the blades, thereby preventing the transfer of excessive heat from the blades. Air is prevented from flowing in the reverse direction by its pressure being higher than that of the combustion gases.

In most cases, the disk is a machined forging of nickel-based alloy, offering high fatigue resistance at elevated temperatures. Although strength increases of about 10% can be achieved using disks of sintered powder, the higher r.p.m. obtainable come at the expense of increased manufacturing costs.

Turbine diameter is decided by compromises between stresses produced at varying r.p.m., weight, and physical size affecting the engine dimensions.

The perimeter of the disk carries turbine blades that are shaped to mate into broached recesses in the disk rim. The blades become red hot and must maintain their strength when subjected to both centrifugal and bending stresses. For this reason, blades are machined from nickel alloy castings.

In service, the gradual permanent elongation of turbine blades is known as "creep." Creep varies with combinations of stress, temperature, and the length of exposure time to those influences. Higher-than-acceptable temperatures, particularly during engine start, will accelerate creep growth and can result in blade failure long before the expected life of the component is reached. [Figure 6-1]

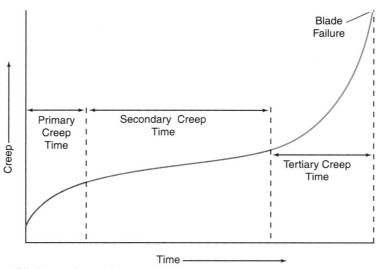

Figure 6-1. Turbine blade creep, if limits are observed.

Turbine blades produce rotation partly by impulse and partly by reaction. Design requirements vary the ratios slightly but 50/50 impulse/reaction is about average for any one blade. The principle of impulse blading depends upon nozzles directing high velocity gases onto turbine blades of a sectional shape, as shown in figure 6-2.

Figure 6-2. Impulse blading.

Without blades in their path, gas streams would exit nozzles in straight lines. In practice, blades catch the emerging gases and turn them in the opposite direction while changing their high entry velocity to a lower exit one. Impulse force is provided by the impact of gases on the blades.

For an impulse-bladed turbine to function optimally, the blades need to be of approximately symmetrical section, and must move past the nozzles at about half the speed at which gases leave the nozzles. Pure impulse turbines are in air driven and cartridge starters.

To use reaction turbine blading of the shapes in figure 6-3, the rotor needs to turn at approximately the same speed as the gases leaving the nozzles. In this way, gases contact the moving blades at a low relative velocity. Due to their airfoil shape, the blades form their own nozzles at their exits. Gases flowing between the moving blades increase their velocity relative to the blades. Acceleration of the gases creates a reactive force in the same fashion as the airplane wing of a cambered airfoil section: the rotor turns in a direction opposite the gases leaving the blades. [Figure 6-3]

Figure 6-3. Reaction turbine blading.

Similar principles apply with either impulse or reaction blading. Gas velocity is first built up in stationary nozzles, then decreased in moving blades. Energy in the hot gases is converted to kinetic energy and then into the mechanical energy of the rotating shaft.

Aircraft GTEs that use turbine blades combining impulse and reaction features need to operate at a compromise speed of between half and full gas nozzle exit speed. This must be done at matching speeds for compressor requirements as pressure ratios vary; that is, when reducing to cruise thrust after climb.

A turbine operates to convert gas energy to mechanical energy, a process which cannot be done 100% efficiently. Thermodynamic and mechanical losses allow a 90 to 92% turbine efficiency to be achieved.

For efficient operation, the tips of turbine blades may reach speeds of 1,500 ft./sec., producing high stresses in rotating parts. It has been estimated that at high rotational speeds, a small turbine blade weighing only two ounces will produce a centrifugal load of two tons on the disk. While turning at high speed, the turbine may be exposed to temperatures of 1,700 degrees Celsius and to gas velocities greater than 2,500 ft./sec.

Turbine blade shrouds are fitted to reduce efficiency losses associated with gas leakage around the tips. [Figure 6-4] Also shown is the commonly used blade-to-disk fir tree type of attachment. With a cold turbine, about .05 inches of movement at the blade tip is allowed by root clearances. At working temperatures, thermal expansion of metal parts tightens the fit of the blade root in the disk. Blades are prevented from sliding out of the disk grooves by side plates, or by pins inserted at an angle through blade roots and disks.

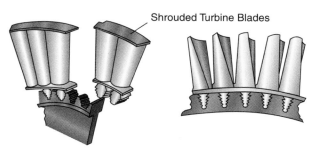

Figure 6-4. Blade shrouds and fir tree attachments.

In addition to the high stresses and temperatures mentioned, turbine blades must withstand high thermal shock, oxidation, corrosion, and fatigue brought on by high-frequency gas flow fluctuations. To withstand the harsh environment, turbine blades must depart from the good aerodynamic shaping of compressor-type blades. Experience has shown that if turbine blade trailing edges are thin, they can crack during starts and stops.

Coating turbine blades with ceramic improves their heat resistance and the engine's efficiency while reducing the amount of cooling air required. Small GTEs have successfully used reinforced ceramic blades, which allow very high turbine entry temperatures (TETs). In larger engines, "single crystal" blades have shown good resistance to creep while accepting increased working temperatures.

Because nozzle guide vanes are not subject to the same rotational stresses as turbine blades, the major factor in manufacturing nozzle guide vanes is heat resistance. Nickel alloys are used, but cooling air from the compressor must still be provided to prevent melting. Nozzle guide vanes are airfoil shaped and located in the turbine case in such a way as to allow expansion.

Turbine blades, like axial flow compressor blades, are given a "twist" so that equal amounts of work are done at all elements along the blade span.

Maximum engine efficiency and performance depend upon careful matching of turbine and compressor flow features; e.g., if nozzle guide vanes produced a back pressure by limiting flow through them, the compressor would be caused to surge. Conversely, too little obstruction to airflow through the nozzle guide vanes would allow higher speeds of flow through the compressor, and possibly lead to it choking.

As a turbine extracts its torque, swirl should be removed from the gas stream exiting the final turbine stage. In this way, smooth axial flow is ensured down the full length of the engine exhaust. Departure from smooth axial flow in the exhaust would introduce turbulence in the flow and vibration in containing components.

Chapter 7

Exhaust

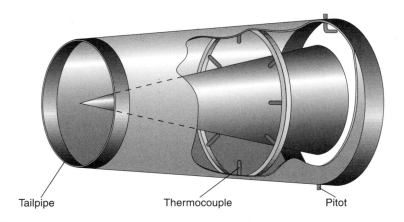

Figure 7-1. Tailpipe.

Discharging gases from an engine at a velocity greater than its turbine discharge velocity increases its thrust. An exhaust pipe's function includes collecting and straightening the gas flow leaving the turbine. When gases enter the pipe, they reduce flow speed by diffusion when acting in conjunction with the tail cone, thereby lowering tailpipe frictional losses. Gas velocity is increased again at the exhaust nozzle for discharge into the atmosphere. Increasing gas velocity in this way increases the engine's thrust. [Figure 7-1]

The tailpipe is a simple stainless steel conical or cylindrical tube that is attached to the engine at the turbine exit. Tailpipe support struts assist in straightening and smoothing the gas flow. Additionally, they carry the shaft rear bearing at their central meeting point.

It is customary to place thermocouples in the tailpipe to measure exhaust gas temperatures (EGTs). With an engine installed in an aircraft, it is not practical to measure the material-limited turbine entry temperature (TET). A good average reading of jet pipe temperature is obtained by taking readings from six to ten thermocouples located around the circumference of the pipe in the gas stream. These thermocouples are wired in parallel to prevent an erroneous EGT reading in case of a thermocouple failure. It would be commercially unrealistic to abort a flight because of an EGT reading failure, and it would be unwise to take off in this state; the parallel wiring makes such a situation unlikely.

Note that by staying within specified EGT limits, the pilot ensures that the upstream turbine entry temperature limits are not being exceeded. The importance of remaining within specified limits cannot be overstated.

On modern turbine engines, pitot dynamic pressure (P1) is taken from the nose of the engine; pitot heads located in the tailpipe give its dynamic pressure (P7). The tailpipe pressure (P7) is divided by the intake pressure (P1) to obtain the engine pressure ratio (EPR). Results obtained from these P7 / P1 readings are presented on cockpit indicators and are of major importance in pilot engine handling. EPR is frequently referred to when quoting engine parameters.

All jet pipes, outlet nozzles, and shapes must be matched to engine requirements because of their influence on TET, mass airflow, exhaust pressure and velocity. Good performance of an engine requires correct relationships between pressure, temperature, and thrust. Nozzle size and shape are important.

When in flight, gas passage into the atmosphere through a converging duct propelling nozzle at high thrusts means gases are accelerated to sonic value at the existing temperature. Consequently, the nozzle becomes choked. No further increase of efflux velocity may occur unless gas temperature increases.

If the upstream total pressure rises above that at which the nozzle chokes, the exit static pressure of the exhaust

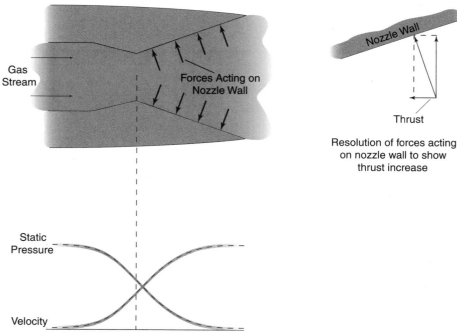

Figure 7-2. Resolution of forces diagram.

rises above atmospheric pressure. The pressure difference acting over the complete area of the nozzle exit produces "pressure thrust," which adds to momentum change thrust. Chapter 21 expands a little upon pressure thrust.

The velocities required for exiting gases are achieved by using exact dimensions for the converging duct exit. Such dimensions are fixed during manufacturing and must not be altered thereafter as engine performance and gas temperatures will be affected.

Some early engines were in fact designed to allow "trimming" to correct r.p.m. or EGT values after entering service. Small metal tabs, to be bent as required, were provided at the exhaust duct nozzle rim. Alternatively, small, adjustable pieces of metal, known as "mice," were fastened around the nozzle perimeter to change its area. Alterations of this nature are only to be done by specially trained technicians.

In Chapter 2, figure 2-6, the principle was shown that, by the use of a CD-shaped component, supersonic flow at exit could be established if a subsonic flow pressure

maintained a gas-to-atmosphere pressure ratio of 2 : 1 or more. Engines use this feature to add to the thrust produced by momentum change. Careful design ensures that weight penalties of a CD exit do not nullify thrust increases.

Figure 7-2 shows the resolution of forces acting on the walls of the diverging section of a CD nozzle. The total of these forces acting in the direction of flight add to thrust. Velocity and static pressure changes through the nozzle are also shown.

Engines with converging duct tailpipes are sometimes fitted with variable area nozzles which open and close automatically in response to fuel flow changes.

Varying flight and engine conditions make gas pressures fluctuate above and below the pressures for which nozzles were designed, and nozzle efficiencies vary accordingly. One solution is to have a nozzle with a variable cross sectional area that may be adjusted for flight conditions. Many adjustable CD nozzles have been tested and fitted to production aircraft. Details of the units are generally not published due to military or proprietary restrictions.

Afterburn is used to boost the static thrust of the engine for takeoff, climb, acceleration, and combat. Its application is almost exclusively for the military field.

To achieve increased thrust, a larger engine could be used but would involve increases in weight, frontal area, and cost. It is preferable to gain the short-term thrust increase by afterburning and accepting the resultant higher fuel flow rates while it functions.

The actual action of afterburning is brought about by supplying and burning extra fuel between the turbine and the jet-propelling nozzle. Practical use is made of the uncombined oxygen remaining in the normal exhaust gases. The resulting temperature increases of the exhaust gases provide increased jet velocity, which translates into greater thrust.

A series of concentric (radial in some cases) manifolds located toward the front end of the afterburner pipe supply fuel. Downstream of the fuel manifolds are the flame holders, which serve to stabilize the flame by providing local flow retardation.

Because flame temperatures at the afterburner can be 1,700° C or higher, burners are arranged in a circle around the longitudinal axis of the jet pipe. As in the combustion chamber, a flow of lower temperature air along the inside of the pipe walls provides cooling.

Cross sectional area of an afterburner pipe is larger than that of the simpler exhaust pipe of an engine lacking afterburn. The larger area ensures that gas velocities remain at manageable values.

Fitting either controllable two-position plug-type or variable-area propelling nozzles allows the afterburning engine to cope with a wide range of operating conditions. There are no pressure buildups to interfere with engine operation.

Fuel spray is fed for even distribution to a number of burners in the pipe flame area. Fuel will not ignite, as might be imagined, due to the hot gas flow. It is initiated by one of three methods:

1. By a catalytic igniter.

2. By an electric igniter plug located close to the burner.

3. By a "hot streak" of flame coming from the engine combustor.

The catalytic igniter creates flames when fuel is sprayed onto a platinum-based igniter element. The igniter plug is like a simple spark plug. The "hot shot" ignition system carries a tongue of flame from the combustor to the afterburn pipe.

Large increases in final thrust allow rapid acceleration and "dash" action by the supersonic aircraft. Fuel consumption rates and the speed achieved are so great that pilots must take care not to be carried so far from base that they have insufficient fuel to return.

It must be possible to ignite the additional fuel in the afterburner pipe under all flight conditions. This means that a stable flame has to be attainable over all possible ranges of mixture strengths and gas flow rates.

Fundamentals of an afterburn engine are shown in figure 8-1. The distance between spray bars and flame holders varies with design. Note that the afterburn pipe may be almost as long as the engine itself.

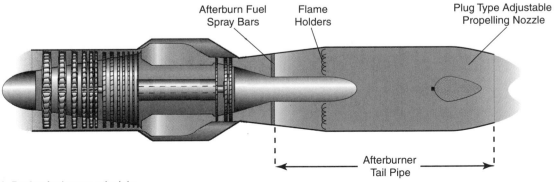

Afterburn Fuel Spray Bars

Flame Holders

Plug Type Adjustable Propelling Nozzle

Afterburner Tail Pipe

Figure 8-1. Basic afterburner principle.

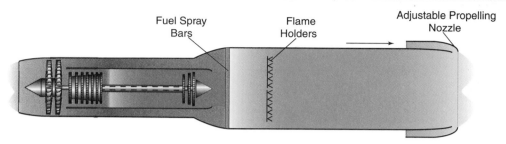

Figure 8-2. Afterburn fan engine.

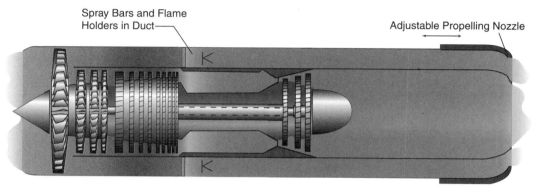

Figure 8-3. Alternative fan afterburner.

When a fan engine is fitted with afterburn, the adopted principle is as shown in figure 8-2.

Fan air and engine core gases join before passing into the afterburner, and pressures of the two streams must be carefully matched. Actual figures, which depend upon engine bypass ratio, can be such that between 30% and 60% of thrust augmentation comes from fan air. Exiting gas velocities are matched by variable area nozzles.

A possible alternative to the bypass arrangement of figure 8-2 is shown in figure 8-3. With this, fuel spray bars and flame holders are located in the bypass duct itself, leading to the occasionally used term, "duct heater." [Figure 8-3]

Yet another variation of fan afterburn has a core gas supplied with afterburn, as in figure 8-1, while the fan air receives separate duct heating. Matching of final temperatures allows the two streams to merge prior to reaching the common exit nozzle.

An afterburn pipe may be of double skin construction, with the outer skin carrying structural loads and the inner carrying thermal stresses. A cooling air stream is induced between the two. Propelling nozzles are attached to afterburn pipes as separate assemblies and will be either two position plug units, as in figure 8-4, or controllable, variable area types.

Heat-resisting nickel alloys are used in the construction of both afterburner pipes and exit nozzles. The pipe has more heat-insulating material than the normal engine jet pipe.

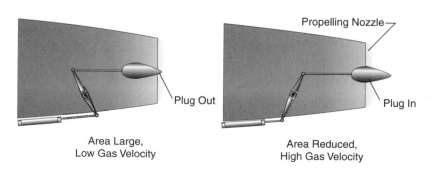

Figure 8-4. Plug-type variable area nozzle.

Chapter 9

Reverse Thrust

Despite the fact that modern aircraft wheel brakes are very good, braking effectiveness is reduced on slippery wet runways and taxiways. Particular care is necessary when maneuvering on snow or ice since brakes are ineffective on large areas of sheet ice. When ice is present on an airfield surface, the obvious thing is to taxi slowly, check wheel braking action frequently, and be prepared to stop without incident if braking action deteriorates to zero. Quick selection of engine reverse thrust may be required to remove any residual forward thrust when the throttles are closed. Some gas turbine engines will produce up to 1,000 lb. of forward thrust with throttles closed.

Using reverse thrust is an effective way of reducing an aircraft's landing run on wet or dry runways. Although not recommended, reverse thrust on a GTE can be maintained until a moving aircraft is brought to a complete halt. Backing an aircraft into a confined space is possible, but requires extreme care and the assistance of ground marshalers.

It is often pointed out that reverse thrust on a jet engine is not as effective as that of a piston engine. Although this is true, jet engine reversal is very useful, and if it does nothing else, it at least kills off forward thrust. Residual thrust can lead to an embarrassing situation when landing on a slippery runway, but stopping without drama is routine with judicial use of reverse thrust. A turboprop achieves reverse thrust by changing propeller blade angles. On a jet aircraft, reverse is achieved by deflecting the gases that exit the engine. In either case, it is unacceptable for the flying pilot to need to look down at the controls when first selecting reverse in landing. Under adverse conditions—such as a fast-moving, heavy aircraft landing at night in a snow shower with a strong gusty cross wind and an icy runway—the pilot simply cannot afford to look around the cockpit. For this reason, reverse actuating systems are interconnected with throttles so that forward and reverse thrusts are controlled by throttle movements. In some aircraft, removal of a reverse lock by the assisting pilot or flight engineer may be necessary to achieve reverse.

The ideal would be to "bend" the engine exhaust 180 degrees, but this is not feasible. It is usual to limit the bending to about 135 degrees, and the retarding component contributes the reverse thrust. Because reverse thrust is only a component of total thrust, any reverse angular movement of a throttle lever at the cockpit quadrant will affect the aircraft less than a similar movement in the forward thrust range.

On a bypass engine, it is normal to reverse only the cold bypass air, because the hot core gases do not contribute largely to thrust. Since cold air is being deflected instead of hot gases, components in this system are constructed with lower heat-resistant materials.

One of these three main methods is used for exhaust gas deflection:

1. Clamshells

2. Buckets

3. Cold stream reversal

Reverse selection and the inclusion of safety features are essentially similar in all three systems.

Clamshells are pneumatically operated using air bled from the engine compressor. [Figure 9-1] They permit

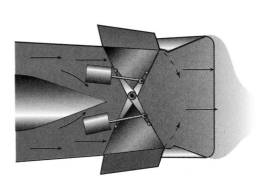

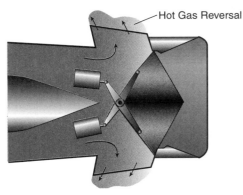

Hot Gas Reversal

Figure 9-1. Clamshells.

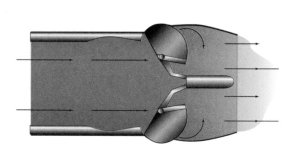

Figure 9-2. Buckets.

an unrestricted flow of gases when the engine is providing forward thrust. In reverse, clamshells rotate to block off the normal gas exit and simultaneously uncover the side, or up and down ducts in which cascade vanes are located.

When in deflect position, increasing throttle movement will provide increasing amounts of reverse thrust. Air leakage from clamshells is nonexistent in the forward thrust position. All functioning of this system is done without lubrication at temperatures up to 600° C, using specially designed door bearings and operating linkages.

The synchronized movement of buckets on any one engine is provided by a single hydraulic ram operating the two buckets by paired push rods. When in the forward thrust position, buckets form part of the divergent passage of the CD nozzle and do not require cascade vanes. Inadvertent reversal is guarded against by having locks in place when in forward thrust. These mechanical locks are withdrawn to allow reverse thrust selection. [Figure 9-2]

In a cold stream reversal system, rear sections of the engine cowls (the "translating cowls") are operated by hydraulic jacks or via flexible cables from an air-driven motor. [Figure 9-3]

In forward thrust, cascade vanes are covered externally by the translating cowls and internally by blocker doors, and cold air flow from the fan has unrestricted passage through the bypass duct. When reverse thrust is selected, the actuation system (hydraulic or pneumatic) moves the translating cowls rearward to expose the exterior of the cascade vanes. At the same time, the interior of the cascade vanes is uncovered when the blocker doors move to blank off the cold stream exit. As a final result, the cold air stream is directed forward by cascade vanes. [Figure 9-4]

Reverse components on a jet engine are bulky, somewhat heavy, and take a little time to be repositioned. It is necessary to allow a second or two between selecting reverse and applying higher thrust. Also, synchronization of reverse across a multi-engine aircraft is not guaranteed. It is necessary to maintain low thrust while checking reverse indicators. Only after all engines are in reverse is it appropriate to increase reverse thrust.

When a multi-engine machine has engines which give considerable residual thrust with closed throttles, it may be acceptable to operate on the ground with one or more engines in idle reverse. This will reduce the heating of wheel brakes since such a machine tends to increase its speed when taxiing.

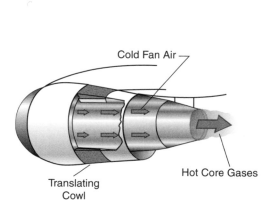

Figure 9-3. Cold stream reverser in forward thrust.

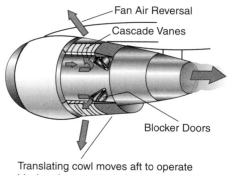

Figure 9-4. Cold stream reverser in operation.

From time to time, an aircraft using pneumatic power for reverse may be shut down with an engine in reverse or not locked in forward thrust. Usually, the engine may be started in the reverse thrust configuration. As the compressor r.p.m. increase, bleed pneumatic pressure will rise to position the reversers in the forward thrust position.

Selecting reverse on a turboprop activates a hydro-mechanical pitch control system that moves the propeller blades to reverse thrust angles of attack. Several safety features are built into a propeller system to prevent inappropriate blade angles in flight. Understanding the systems that apply is most important. Automatic "trimming" of fuel supply to the engine takes place when reverse is selected. This ensures a balanced output of engine power as blade angles change, and prevents over-speeding of the engine when blade angles are close to zero thrust values. Considerable advances have been made in turboprop design in recent years, and there are many differences in detail between applications in aircraft. Students of a new type of machine must make themselves thoroughly conversant with engine/propeller details during their type-conversion training.

Both clamshell and bucket systems are subjected to high gas loads combined with high gas temperatures. Robust construction with heat-resisting materials is necessary.

Cold stream system components are not exposed to high temperatures, so they are constructed of comparatively light materials such as aluminum or its alloys. The cowling of cold stream reversal engines is usually double skinned, and the space between the skins is filled with noise-absorbing material.

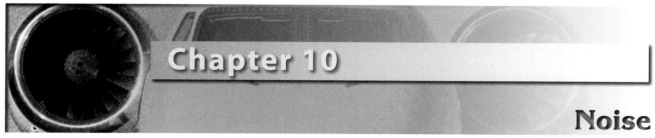

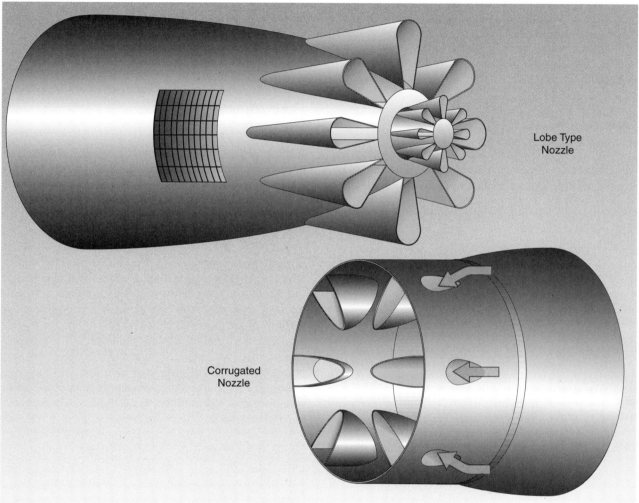

Figure 10-1. Basic noise suppressors.

Increasingly in recent years, aircraft noise has become an issue of consequence. Airport noise regulations, many of which originate from complaints by residents of surrounding areas, have led directly to considerable research on GTE noise suppression.

Major airports have sound recording stations located at strategic points along departure and arrival routes for each runway. Airport authorities publish acceptable levels of noise for each point. It is standard noise-abatement practice for aircraft to overfly noise-measuring stations at specified minimum altitudes and at prescribed maximum power settings.

"Hushkitting" of older engines is done to keep expensive airframes in service while meeting the increasingly restrictive engine noise regulations. [Figure 10-1] The last of the big piston-engine commercial aircraft seldom had service lives exceeding 20 years because of escalating maintenance costs. Continual vibration from their engines produced their rapid aging. With today's almost vibration-free turbine engines, airframe lives in excess of 30 years are more commonplace.

Pilots can be certain that the consequences of engine noise will become significant features in their lives when they fly aircraft using gas turbine engines.

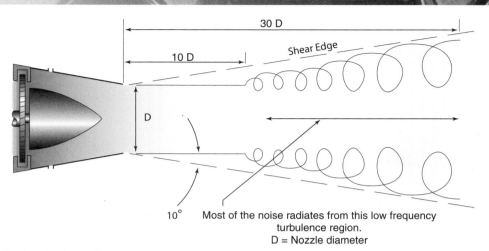

Figure 10-2. Hot exhaust noise patterns.

The unit used in noise measurement is the Effective Perceived Noise Decibel (EPNdB). Its definition is of no concern here, but its application is of major concern.

There are three main noise producing areas connected with a GTE:

1. Fan or compressor

2. Turbine

3. Exhaust

Noise produced by these sources varies from one engine type to the next. All three increase their noise output as airflow velocity through the engine rises.

Exhaust noise has received the most attention from research workers because it increases more rapidly as airflow velocities increase.

Exhaust noise originates in the zones of high turbulence, which arise from shear action at the boundaries where the high-speed jet and the atmosphere meet. High-frequency noise comes from small eddies near the exhaust duct, and lower-frequency noise occurs further downstream where there are larger eddies. [Figure 10-2] In addition, a regular pattern of shock waves forms within the jet exhaust core when its velocity exceeds local M 1.0. The shock wave pattern produces a single-frequency tone and some amplification of particular frequencies in the noise mixing region.

Compressor and turbine noises come from pressure fields and turbulent wakes of gases that have passed over rotating blades and stationary vanes.

Specific tones originate from the regular passage of rotor blade wakes over their downstream stages, with each stage generating its own particular tones and harmonics. Clearance spaces between rotor blades and stator vanes will influence the intensity of the wake noise.

If these distances are kept small, strong pressure field interaction takes place to produce a powerful tone. The wake of a high bypass engine fan produces tones of this type, but because of the lower velocities present and the larger separation between fan blades and static vanes, the noise is not high intensity.

Turbine and compressor noise is only of consequence when an engine is operating at low thrust, as when on the ramp or taxiing. They are of little concern because exhaust noise predominates. However, compressor and turbine noise become more apparent in the bypass engine as its exhaust noise is reduced. As bypass engines become larger, the internal work done by their compressors and turbines will increase, and the noise generated by these components will become more obvious. This takes place when bypass ratios exceed approximately 5:1.

Noise from combustion section burners can also be quite large, but since the units are located close to the core of the engine, other noises tend to smother it.

METHODS OF NOISE SUPPRESSION

Noise is suppressed by reducing the exhaust jet velocity relative to the atmosphere, or by increasing the mixing rate. In addition to lowering exhaust noise by its dispersion, manufacturers also aim to lower the amount of noise produced in the engine and to contain as much as possible with sound absorbing materials. Shortening its region of mixing with the atmosphere and increasing the mixing rate lowers the exhaust noise.

High-frequency noises are rapidly absorbed in the atmosphere. Some high-frequency noises are beyond the human audible range but can be heard by animals, including birds, which seem to enjoy flocking near airports. Ingestion of seagull-sized birds could cause the failure of an axial-flow engine. Pilots must be aware of

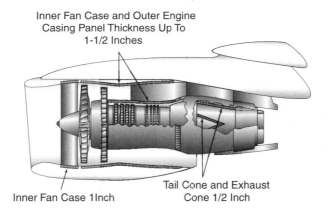

Inner Fan Case and Outer Engine
Casing Panel Thickness Up To
1-1/2 Inches

Inner Fan Case 1Inch

Tail Cone and Exhaust
Cone 1/2 Inch

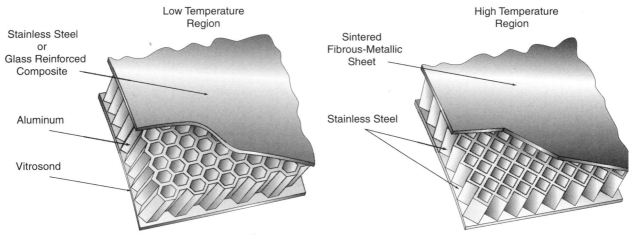

Low Temperature
Region

Stainless Steel
or
Glass Reinforced
Composite

Aluminum

Vitrosond

High Temperature
Region

Sintered
Fibrous-Metallic
Sheet

Stainless Steel

Figure 10-3. This figure illustrates common areas on a turbine engine where noise suppression materials are located. Noise suppression materials convert acoustic energy (pressure) to friction heat energy.

the hazardous nature of bird ingestion on takeoff. The fact that GTEs are noisy provides no protection.

While the high-frequency noises within the audible range of humans can be very disturbing, it is fortunate that their intensity is short lived.

The two types of noise suppressors shown in figure 10-1 break up the single exhaust stream into a number of smaller jets and increase the jet-to-atmosphere contact area. This reduces the size of the eddies formed and raises the sound frequency without altering the total noise energy.

With its two exhaust streams, the high bypass engine inherently produces less noise. Nevertheless, the same principles already mentioned apply to these engines for reducing noise further. Mixing the ejected hot and cold streams through a single outlet has proven to lower the bypass engine's exhaust noise: a method not suitable for large diameter fans. Having a low level of exhaust-generated noise, the high bypass engine's fan and turbine are its major producers of noise.

Continual research has provided many answers in the field of engine noise reduction. Bypass fan and turbine noises are minimized by reducing the airflow turbulence and the interaction between rotating and stationary blades, while at the same time, making full use of acoustic linings.

Materials achieve their acoustic absorbency by converting acoustic energy into heat energy. The usual acoustic lining for an engine is composed of perforated layers of thin steel, titanium, or aluminum separated by honeycombs of aluminum or stainless steel. During manufacture, the lining is bonded around the engine and inside the cowls. Sometimes composite materials are utilized for sound absorption linings. [Figure 10-3]

However, acoustic linings produce a higher consumption of fuel because of increases in weight and skin friction, but the sound absorption is considered to compensate for the additional fuel used.

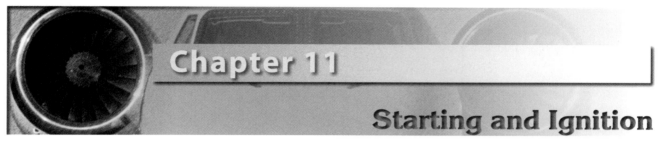

Chapter 11

Starting and Ignition

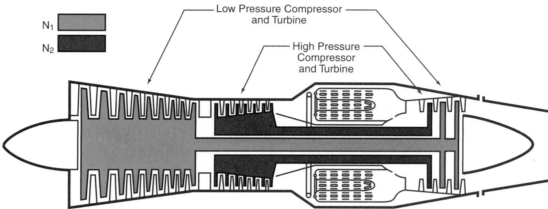

Figure 11-1. Two spool axial flow engine.

Starting a GTE calls for two separate systems when it is stationary on the ground:

1. Only the HP turbine/compressor assembly spool is mechanically connected to the starter. The HP turbine/compressor must be rotated up to sufficient r.p.m. to pass enough air through the engine for it to function independently.

2. There must be some system of ignition to commence burning of the air/fuel mixture in the combustor.

For normal starting, the two systems will operate in unison. When start is initiated, the systems are coordinated and completely controlled by electric circuits. [Figure 11-1]

Throughout the whole start sequence, the pilot initiating the action must monitor not only the exhaust gas temperature (EGT) but also its rate of increase. A few starts in a simulator, or in the aircraft itself, will allow the pilot to rapidly learn what is a normal rate of EGT increase. If an abnormally fast EGT increase is noted, the fuel supply to the engine must be cut immediately. Cockpit temperature indicators lag behind the actual turbine inlet temperature during a "hot start." If the pilot waits until EGT is at a maximum before cutting the fuel, overheating of the turbine will have already occurred. The engine will be unserviceable and will require replacement. [Figure 11-2]

Although some of the latest engines have almost com-

Figure 11-2. Turbine exhaust gas temperature (EGT) gauge.

pletely automatic starting systems, the following sequence of start actions is provided as a general guide to earlier engines. This sequence of actions for starting a typical two-spool bypass engine is given for general information. Each particular engine type will have its own specific sequence to follow.

Typical actions for engine start on the ground:

- Throttle *closed.*
- Start lever *closed.*
- Fuel supply and booster pump *on.*
- Starter master on to *arm* electric circuitry.
- Starter motor engaged to rotate N_2.

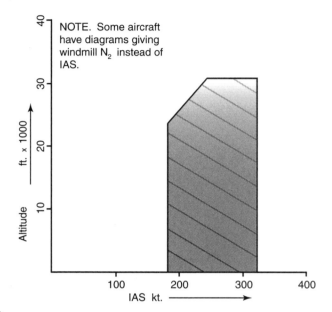

Figure 11-3. Relight envelope.

- Confirm indication of N_2 *rotating*.

- Confirm N_1 *rotating*, ensures N_1 system not binding.

- At 15% N_2, *open* start lever to provide fuel and ignition.

- Note light up at 18% N_2, EGT rising.

- Carefully monitor the RATE of EGT *rise*.

- At 38% N_2, the starter should *cut out* automatically; if no,

- Starter cut out by 40% N_2, start lever to *closed*.

- In normal, start engine accelerates to idle at 55% N_2.

- Starter master *off*.

Although normal starts on the ground require contributions from both the starter and ignition systems, it must be possible to operate each independently. If it is suspected that a stationary engine on the ground has some unburned fuel remaining in it, a ventilating cycle will be necessary to ensure that a "hot start" does not occur on the next start attempt. For such a "blow out," as it is known, the engine is rotated by engaging the starter with the start lever in the cut-off position to prevent fuel flow and ignition.

To relight the engine while airborne, with the engine(s) windmilling, there is no need to rotate the engine by using the starter motor. In fact, attempting to engage a starter motor on a rotating engine will usually damage the starter mechanism. All jet aircraft cockpits are supplied with a relight envelope diagram, as in figure 11-3; some plot N_2 r.p.m. against altitude, while others plot airspeed against altitude.

In either case, using the diagram is simple. By putting the aircraft "within the envelope," relight is assured unless the engine is defective. So, for an airborne engine start, ignition is required but not the starter motor.

The moment at which ignition is supplied during a start cycle varies with the engine type. On some, the ignition is on from the commencement of cranking, while on others, forward movement of the start lever will initiate ignition. Any time a choice exists, ignition must be on before, or at latest, with the supply of fuel.

STARTERS

While all GTEs start with similar procedures, the required engine rotation will be supplied by one of several different starter methods:

1. An electric starter motor will normally be DC. Applied voltage builds up progressively as the engine accelerates. When it reaches self-sustaining speed, the load on the starter is reduced and the starting cycle is cancelled. [Figure 11-4]

2. The air starter has some military applications and is most commonly used in commercial aircraft. [Figure 11-5] It is economical, light, and simple to operate. An air starter can be thought of as an air-driven turbine connected to the N_2 assembly. Air can be supplied to the starter from any of three sources:

   (a) From an Auxiliary Power Unit (APU). The APU is a permanent part of the aircraft's equipment. It is a miniature GTE from which pneumatic and electric supplies are drawn for operating aircraft services on the ground. It is independent of external needs.

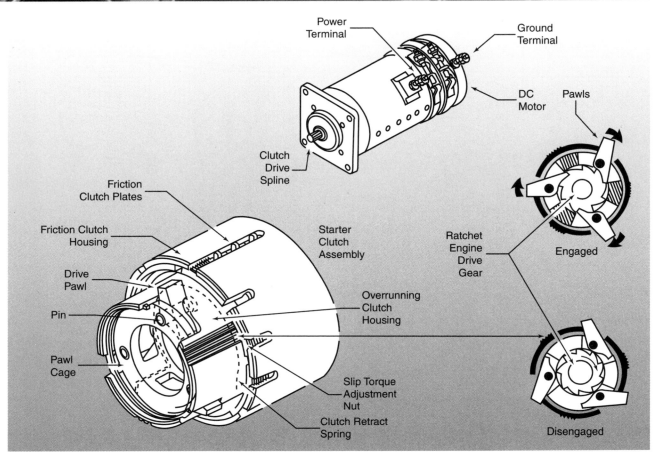

Figure 11-4. Electric starter.

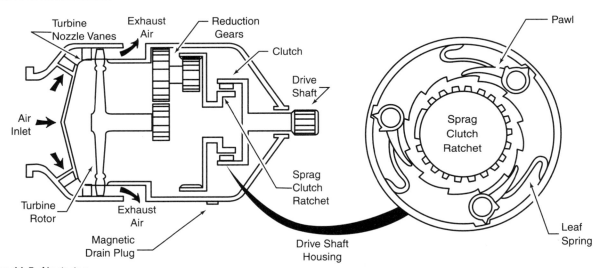

Figure 11-5. Air starter.

(b) By cross-bleeding from another engine. With appropriate switching, an operating engine can be given sufficient r.p.m. to supply air to the starter of the stationary engine.

(c) From an external ground supply; either starter-wagon or bottles. Generally, a starter-wagon will have a sufficient capacity to start all engines. When bottles are used, the capac-ity may be too low to start all engines, even though the pressure may be quite high. In this case, the first engine can be started from the bottles and the cross-bleed used for the remainder.

An operating cockpit crew can find it useful to have their aircraft independent of ground support, particu-larly with crowded airports following large-scale flight

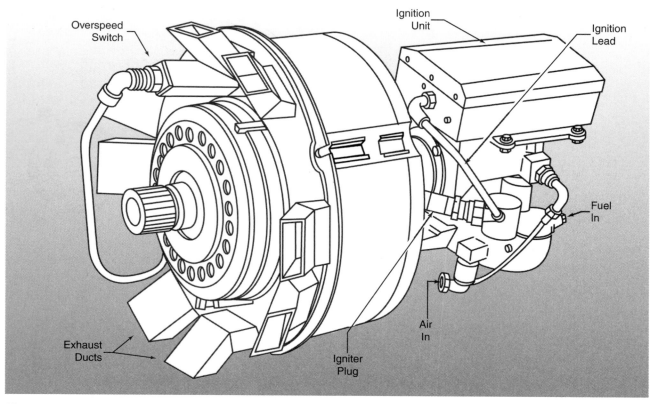

Figure 11-6. Gas turbine starter.

diversions. Some engines that utilize air starters have an additional small combustor unit fitted to each engine. When air is not available to start the engines, fuel for this combustor is drawn from the engine and high-pressure air is drawn from an on-board bottle. These are fed to the combustor and ignited. The resulting hot gases are directed onto the turbine of the air starter to achieve its rotation. Upon completion of the engine start, an electric circuit cuts off fuel and air to the combustor.

3. Again, a gas turbine starter is a miniature GTE. The unit is self-contained with its own oil, fuel, ignition and starting systems. It will probably have a reverse flow combustor feeding a turbine that drives a centrifugal compressor. A free turbine starts the aircraft engine via reduction gears, clutch, and shafting. A second type of gas turbine starter is fueled by a so-called "mono" fuel; i.e., one supplying its own oxygen for combustion. The fuel is iso-propyl-nitrate and is hazardous to those handling it. It does have limited military applications because its high amount of energy provides rapid engine starts. [Figure 11-6]

4. A cartridge starter is for military use since the system is completely independent of ground support. Widely separated dispersal points can be occupied without the need for exterior assistance.

Cartridges look like oversized shotgun cartridges and are electrically fired. They are held in a rotatable block that carries several cartridges in the same fashion as a revolver handgun. Successive starts can be made by rotating the block to present live cartridges to the firing breech. When the cordite charge is detonated, a flow of hot gases goes to a small impulse turbine, which rotates the aircraft engine via reduction gearing and a clutch. [Figure 11-7]

5. Hydraulic starters are sometimes used for small GTEs. A hydraulic unit, which is a pump in normal engine operation, receives oil at its usual outlet point to run "in reverse" as a motor, which rotates the engine through shafting and gears. Once again, the starter cycle is electrically controlled. The hydraulic unit reverts to being a pump at the end of the start sequence.

Some engines have no separate starter. N_2 rotation is achieved by directing a jet of high-pressure air onto the turbine of the engine itself.

IGNITION

Jet engines make use of High Energy (HE) ignition systems, and all are fitted with dual systems. Low voltage

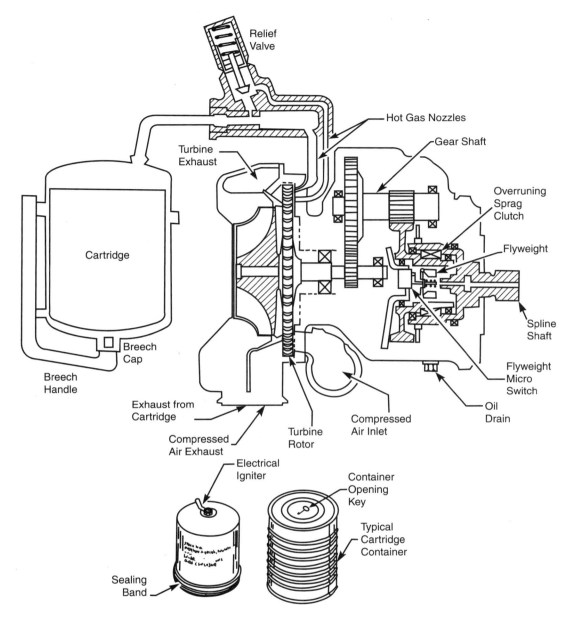

Figure 11-7. Cartridge starter.

current is supplied to each HE ignition unit. This is transformed and stored until energy is released at ignition as a high-voltage, high-amperage discharge across the points of the igniter plug. In this respect, the igniter plug is similar to the spark plug of piston engines.

Igniter plugs are rated in joules, and their output may be varied to meet operational requirements. One joule is 1 watt-second. The normal rate of plug discharge is anything from 60 to 100 sparks per minute. Any electric discharge points that are subject to repeated arcing will pit one electrode and have a deposit buildup on the other. GTE igniters have this problem. The working life of igniters is extended by limiting the energy at the arcing points.

Under abnormally adverse start conditions, such as very cold weather or high altitude re-lights, an igniter may require as much as 12 joules. Yet when an igniter is used as a precaution on takeoff, in heavy rain, snow, or turbulence, continuous ignition of only 3 to 6 joules is required and may be used for an hour or more.

Most engines have one high-output igniter of perhaps 20 joules and a low-output one of perhaps 4 joules. Both operate during engine start and only the low output igniter operates during continuous ignition. On other engines, both igniters are capable of high and low output. Igniters may be AC and operated by a transformer, or DC, using a vibrator unit or a transistorized chopper unit.

Figure 11-8. High tension igniter plug (A), low tension igniter plug (B).

Two types of igniter plug are in use [Figure 11-8]:

1. The high tension type is similar to an ordinary spark plug, but it has a larger gap that requires about 25,000 volts to provide the ionization that allows a spark to bridge the gap.

2. The low tension type provides a low resistance path for energy stored in a condenser. It operates at about 2,000 volts.

Stopping a jet engine is simple. All that is needed is to retard the throttle fully and cut the fuel supply by closing the start lever.

AUXILIARY POWER UNIT (APU)

The auxiliary power unit (APU) is a miniature GTE. An APU is usually located in the aft fuselage with its exhaust passing into the atmosphere at the extreme tail. Its purpose is to supply electricity and conditioning air for the cabin at any time the propulsive engines are not operating.

An electric generator that runs off the APU allows all electrics on the aircraft to be fully functional on the ground. Conditioning air warms the cabin in sub-zero temperatures and cools it in tropical places. In addition to having engine-driven hydraulic pumps, many aircraft have electrically operated pumps that pressurize hydraulic systems prior to engine start. For example, parking brakes (wheels) may be set on before start-up.

Like most equipment connected with aircraft, APUs are constantly being improved and are becoming more sophisticated. In principle, they remain simple, miniature GTEs.

Chapter 12

Fuel

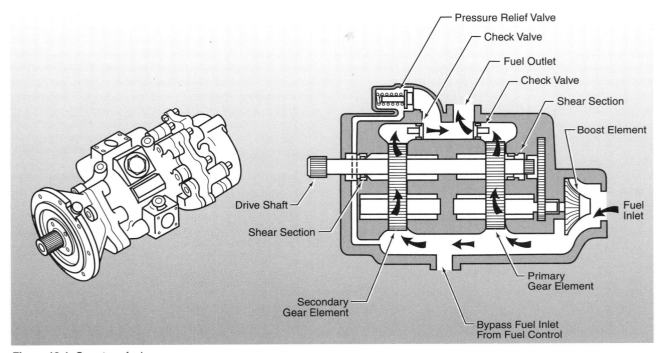

Figure 12-1. Gear-type fuel pump.

A booster pump sends low-pressure fuel from a tank (at about 20 to 30 p.s.i.) to the engine where it supplies the engine-driven pump. The function of the booster pump is to supply fuel at a flow rate and pressure that will enable the engine to operate under all possible flight conditions. The supply system typically includes:

- A low-pressure (booster) pump that delivers fuel under pressure from the tank to the engine without cavitation or vapor-locking.

- A fuel-cooled oil cooler (not all installations).

- An air-heated fuel heater.

- A fuel filter, possibly with its own heater.

- Transmitters for fuel flow, temperature, and pressure.

- Cockpit indicators for fuel flow, temperature, and pressure.

At the engine, fuel from the low-pressure system is accepted by the engine-driven pump, which raises the pressure to several hundred p.s.i. Thus, high-pressure fuel is available to the fuel control unit (FCU) for fuel-

operated servo functions and for supply to the combustion burners.

The most often used and lightest engine-driven fuel pump is the gear type. Its output is directly proportional to r.p.m. and it is classed as a positive displacement pump. Excess fuel is passed back from the pump outlet to its inlet to control the fuel flow to the burner spray nozzles. Bypass action is effected by a spill valve, which is sensitive to pressure drops across controlling units in the system, and opens or closes to regulate spill as required. [Figure 12-1]

Another frequently used positive displacement pump is the plunger type in which output depends upon:

- The speed of rotation.

- The stroke of the plungers.

A plunger-type pump consists of a rotor assembly, or cylinder block, fitted with several plungers. The shaped ends of the plungers protrude beyond the bores of the cylinders that are machined in the block and bear against a non-rotating cam plate. Because of the inclination of the cam plate, reciprocating action is provided to the plungers as the cylinder block rotates. Pumping action is produced in this way. Fuel servo operation varies the cam plate inclination, which determines the stroke of the plungers, and hence the pump output. The cam-plate-actuating piston receives servo pressure on its spring side and pump delivery pressure on the other side. Variations in the pressure differences across the servo piston determine the inclination of the plate to vary the plunger strokes. Inclination of the plate is given spring bias to the full stroke position of the plungers in the event of servo failure. In this way, engine thrust will not be limited by pump output.

A plunger-type fuel pump can produce flow rates varying from 100 to 2,000 gallons per hour at maximum pressure (about 2,000 p.s.i.). Such a pump can absorb as much as 60 HP in its normal running.

FUEL HEATING

Kerosene fuels are capable of holding minute particles of water in solution and/or suspension. Even if all water were removed during the refining process, some would re-enter the fuel upon exposure to the atmosphere. It is not possible for fuel in the aircraft tanks to be completely water-free. At low temperatures, trapped water particles may turn to ice and lodge in fuel filters to restrict engine fuel supply.

Many aircraft engines include combined fuel heater/oil cooler units located between the booster pumps and fuel filter inlets; cooling the engine lubricating oil raises the fuel temperature. [Figure 12-2] If the amount of heat added from the engine oil is insufficient to melt all the ice, fuel or fuel-filter heaters receiving hot air from engine compressors may be added to aircraft systems. Air temperature is thermostatically controlled to provide the required amount of heat.

FUEL CONTROL

Engine thrust selection is made through the throttle, using maximum r.p.m. for takeoff and required EPR settings for the remainder of flight. As in piston engines, controlling the amount of fuel fed to the com-

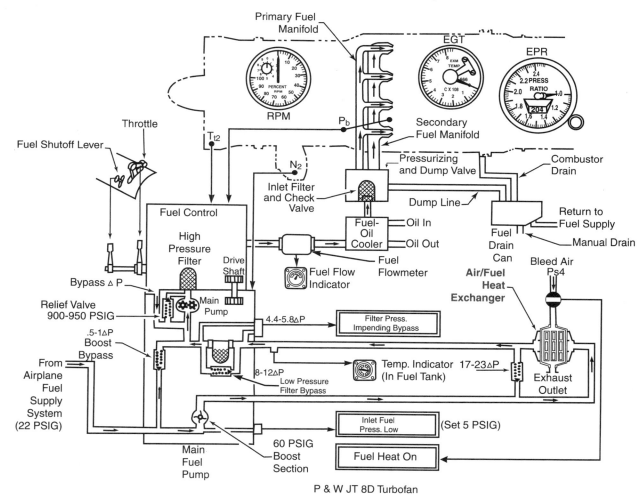

Figure 12-2. Fuel system including air/fuel heat exchanger.

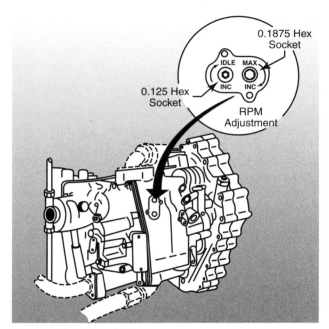

Figure 12-3. Fuel control.

bustion chambers determines the output of thrust. Opening the throttle increases fuel pressure to the combustor nozzles and produces a greater fuel flow. The gas temperature increases, which in turn increases the acceleration of that gas, the engine r.p.m., and the total airflow. The interrelationships of controlling devices are fully automatic and regulated by the fuel control unit (FCU). [Figure 12-3] The varying changes of air density brought on by speed, altitude, and ambient temperature alterations add to the total complexity. Practical engine handling would not be possible without these automatic operations. A malfunctioning FCU, which is uncommon, is removed and returned for correction to specially approved workshops. Only minor adjustments by trained technicians are permitted in the field. This task is NOT for pilots.

Six methods of automatic fuel control are mentioned here in name only. Functioning details are the concern of specialists.

- Pressure control (turbojet).
- Pressure control (turboprop).
- Flow control.
- Combined acceleration and speed control.
- Pressure ratio control.
- Electronic engine control.

In a turboprop, changes in engine r.p.m. and propeller pitch need to be coordinated since both influence power output. Throttle and propeller are interconnected

to provide the correct relationship between air and fuel flows. It is normal for maximum engine r.p.m. to be limited by the propeller speed controller. A governor that limits the fuel supply prevents overspeeding of the engine.

It should be noted that fuel serves as a lubricant for the engine pump. If fuel has been cut off to the engine in flight as an action against fire, it is recommended that it be re-supplied every half-hour for pump lubrication. (The engine will be windmilling, so the pump continually operates.) Of course, it is necessary to allow the engine to cool thoroughly before re-supplying fuel.

FUEL SPRAY NOZZLES

Fuel spray nozzles (FSN) atomize the fuel entering the combustor. Many have different-sized outlet orifices: small diameter holes for lower fuel flows, and larger diameter holes for higher flow rates under pressure increases. [Figure 12-4]

A "spill" type of FSN incorporates a passage that spills fuel away from the swirl chamber as the demand decreases with altitude increase. The swirl was introduced to ensure the efficient and constant atomizing of fuel.

THE EFFECT OF CHANGING FUEL TYPE

GTEs can operate on almost any fuel that may be fed to them: gasoline, diesel oil, natural gas, pulverized coal dust, kerosene, even peanut oil has been suggested, although many peanuts would be wasted. That does not mean you can refuel your aircraft with diesel or even aviation gasoline.

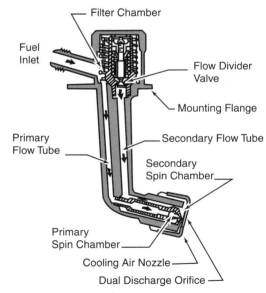

Figure 12-4. Fuel spray nozzle.

Like any other aircraft fuel, aviation gas turbine fuel must be produced to very strict specifications in order to combine safety, optimum engine performance, and good engine life. The amount of heat available in each weight unit of fuel (pound or kilogram) is almost the same for all fuels that are approved for use in aircraft gas turbines. Because of this, the heat value available per unit of volume (gallon or liter) can be obtained by comparing the specific gravity (SG) of the fuels.

- Jet Fuel SG = approx. .82
- AVGAS SG = approx. .72

Specific gravity of one grade of fuel will vary from place to place, depending on the geographical location of the oil field from which the crude oil was obtained. Minor variations of SG within one grade of turbine fuel should not concern an operating pilot. However, changing from aviation kerosene to aviation gasoline, for example, could cause considerable consequences, and such changes are not normally sanctioned. The main effect on a GTE of changing fuel type is due to this SG variation, i.e. the varying heat units available per gallon or liter of fuel.

With a centrifugal-type speed governor on an engine, increasing SG will result in an increase in centrifugal pressure on the governor diaphragm. The governor will act to reduce engine r.p.m. Resetting the governor will be required with a new fuel. A decrease of SG would influence the governor to allow higher engine r.p.m., perhaps higher than the engine maximum. In this case, the pilot may need to decrease throttle opening to maintain the engine within r.p.m. limits.

Using a combined acceleration and speed control FCU, the pressure drop governor is density compensated. Fuel is metered on mass flow and not volume flow. No FCU adjustment is necessary when making a change of fuel.

If a lower grade of fuel is used other than the one specified, it can produce excess carbon, greater flame temperature, and higher metal temperatures in the combustor and downstream. The lives of the turbine and combustor would be reduced.

REQUIREMENTS OF FUELS

There are two classes of approved GTE fuels:

- Kerosene-type.
- Wide-cut gasoline-type.

The term "wide-cut" refers to the practice of taking a liquid from the fractionating column in the oil refinery

that condenses over a wider range of temperatures than a normal aviation gasoline. By using wide-cut boundaries, more aviation fuel is obtained per barrel of crude oil. However, kerosene-type jet fuel is the most often encountered.

To easily start an engine, fuel leaving the spray nozzles must be ignited without difficulty. Quality control during refining will ensure that the fuel is volatile, i.e. it will vaporize easily at low temperatures (this feature depends on the fuel's viscosity). Combined with good pressure and atomizer design, a volatile fuel will start the engine well under all operating conditions and will provide efficient combustion. It must be possible to pump GTE fuels without difficulty, which means that fuel viscosity must be acceptable at very low temperatures. Low temperatures of -60° C or less are possible at higher altitudes and latitudes. Fortunately, it can take several hours for tank temperatures to "cold soak" down to such values.

Calorific value is an expression of the heat energy released during complete combustion of one pound or one gallon of fuel. When aircraft tank capacity is the limiting factor, calorific value per unit volume should be as high as possible. When an aircraft's payload is limited by the total acceptable weight, the calorific value per unit of fuel weight should be as high as possible.

GTE fuels tend to corrode the components of fuel and combustor systems, mainly because of the presence of sulfur and water. Burning sulfur in air produces sulfur dioxide. Combined with water, this creates sulfurous acid, which is extremely corrosive to lead and copper. It is not practicable to remove all sulfur and water from fuel during its production. The quantities of these contaminants must be rigorously limited, however.

As already noted, kerosene fuel must act as a lubricant to moving parts of a fuel system. This is done over the whole working range of temperatures.

Fire precautions must be strictly observed on the ground and in flight. Remember that, although kerosene is not as easy to ignite as gasoline, it can be dangerously combustible.

BOILING AND VAPOR LOCKING

Volatility is the principal difference between kerosene and wide-cut fuels. Wide-cuts have a higher volatility, and consequently, an increased tendency to boil and vapor lock. Having a low vapor pressure, kerosene will boil only at high altitudes or temperatures. Wide-cuts have lower values.

During any flight, fuel temperature will vary depending on:

- Fuel temperature at the time of loading, ground time, and exposure to solar heating.

- Rate of climb.

- Flight altitude and time spent at that altitude.

- Heating due to aircraft forward speed.

The loss of fuel quantity due to boiling can be very high when using wide-cuts, resulting in vapor locking and the consequent malfunctioning of engine fuel systems and fuel metering items. Fuel tanks on aircraft may be pressurized to reduce the risk of boiling fuel. The space above the fuel in the tank is held at a pressure that is greater than the fuel's vapor pressure at the existing temperature. To achieve pressurization, either a tank's venting may be restricted, or an inert gas under pressure may be applied to the tank.

Lengthy supersonic flights require some form of heat insulation for tanks in order to prevent excessive temperature increases in them.

FUEL CONTAMINANTS

Good storage procedures and frequent, routine checks of aircraft tank water drains ensure that satisfactory fuel gets to the engines. Solid matter and free water contamination will be reduced to very low levels by using filters, fuel/water separators, and appropriate additives.

Cutting down on solids suspended in a fuel reduces pump wear while lowering the possibility of system blockage (corrosion is also reduced). Microbiological growths, commonly termed "fungus" in the industry, caused anxiety some years ago due to their presence in fuel systems. Using additives and reducing the amounts of undissolved water in the fuel have almost removed the problem.

Chapter 13

Lubrication

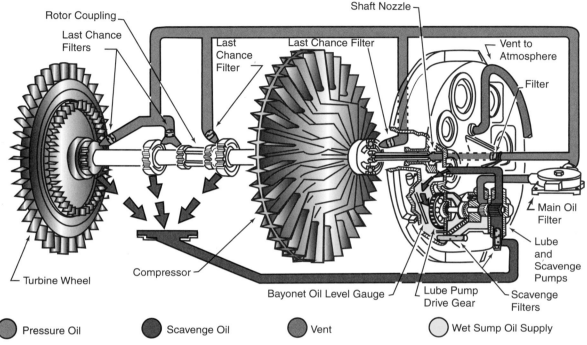

Figure 13-1. Lubrication system.

● Pressure Oil   ● Scavenge Oil   ● Vent   ○ Wet Sump Oil Supply

Almost all gas turbine engines (GTEs) make use of self-contained recirculatory oil systems in which fluid is distributed to engine parts, and returned to oil tanks, by pressure and scavenge pumps. In addition to lubricating engine moving parts, oil must also carry away excess heat, supply a protective film to surfaces subject to corrosion, and collect in the tank sump matter which could lead to failure if permitted to remain in gear boxes and bearing housings. [Figure 13-1]

Furthermore, turboprop engine oil must lubricate reduction gears, which are under heavy load. A more viscous oil is required. After having its pressure boosted by a governor pump, turboprop oil is used to operate the propeller pitch change mechanism.

In the common recirculatory systems, there are two basic types:

1. The pressure relief valve system. [Figure 13-2]

2. The full flow system.

The main difference between the two systems is in the manner of control of oil flow to the bearings. In both,

oil temperature and pressure are critical to the safe handling of an engine, so cockpit indications are provided.

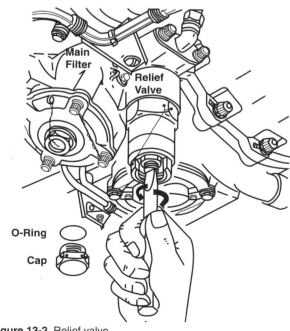

Figure 13-2. Relief valve.

1. By design, the pressure relief valve (PRV) system restricts the feed line pressure to the bearings to a definite value. The relief valve opens at a predetermined pressure to return some oil to the tank, and a constant feed pressure to the bearings is provided. Some engines using this pressure relief valve system will vary the valve setting with engine r.p.m. As the r.p.m. increases, the valve opening is delayed until a higher pressure is reached, which maintains a constant flow rate to the bearings.

2. Engines in which bearing chamber pressures rise markedly with r.p.m. increase require an alternative to the PRV system; this is a full-flow system which operates without a pressure relief valve. By using smaller pressure and scavenge pumps of sufficient capacity, the full-flow system provides adequate oil at maximum engine r.p.m. This reduction in sizes is possible because there is no pressure relief valve spillage to be processed. Full-flow systems are used in most turbofan engines.

A few types of special application engines use a total loss, or expendable, system of lubrication. Intermittent shots of oil are sent to parts of the engine where required, then spilled outside the engine after lubrication. This method of lubrication is limited to use on engines operating for a short duration only, such as booster and vertical lift engines. A feature of the expendable system is that weight penalties are low and the system is simple. It has no need for coolers, scavenge pumps, or filters.

Some engines make use of a spring-loaded plunger type of pump for delivery of a continuous flow of oil to the bearings. Other engines deliver a single shot of oil from a piston pump that is operated by fuel pressure when the start lever is moved to "open" during engine start. Oil is delivered to the front and rear bearings, and after lubricating all the components, it is dumped either into the gas stream or into a reservoir to be drained overboard after engine shutdown. The single-shot pump piston may be returned to its original position after use by a second simple coiled spring.

COMPONENTS OF OIL SYSTEMS

An oil tank is usually a separate component mounted on the engine, which may, however, be integral with an external gear box. Included in an oil tank are refill and drain points, a sight gauge or dipstick, a filter, and a de-aerator. Dipsticks are mostly calibrated to show the quantity of oil that needs to be added to bring the reservoir back up to its normal operating level. GTEs use expensive synthetic lubricating oils. Any unused oil should be discarded to avoid its possible subsequent contamination. Oil consumption is very low in comparison to a piston engine. Often it is possible to fly for several hours before even a small top-off of the reservoir becomes necessary. [Figure 13-3]

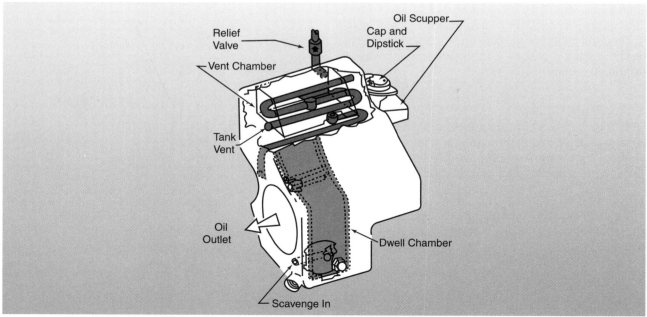

Figure 13-3. Oil reservoir.

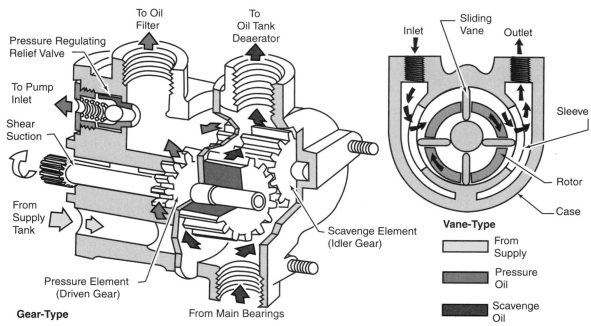

Figure 13-4. Oil pumps.

It is essential that oil pumps continue to function at all times when an aircraft engine is operating. Pump drive shafts do not include a feature that makes deliberate shear in service possible. A single pressure pump may be sufficient for an engine's needs. Several scavenge pumps, one for each engine chamber, are normal for coping with the larger volume of oil to be scavenged as a result of air bubbles introduced to the fluid by sealing air. Gear-type pumps are usually used for both pressure and scavenge purposes, but vane or gerotor types may be used. [Figure 13-4]

Oil coolers remove heat from the oil by passing ambient air, or fuel that is en route to the engine, through the cooler core. Filters and oil coolers are protected from excessively high pressure damage, which might occur with filter blockage or very cold conditions, by pressure limiting bypass valves. Cockpit warning lights indicate pending or actual bypass. [Figure 13-5]

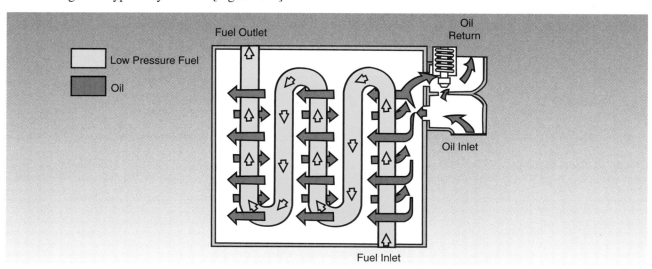

Figure 13-5. Oil to fuel heat exchanger.

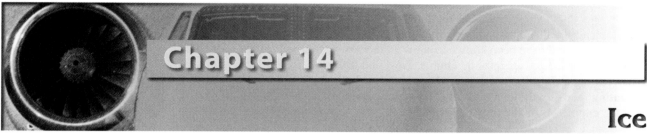

Chapter 14

Ice

Engine pressure ratio (EPR) is P7/P1, i.e. tailpipe pressure / pitot pressure at the nose of the engine. Any interference with P1 will cause variations in EPR indications. Ice blocking the P1 inlet hole will cause an increase in the cockpit's EPR indication as pressure bleeds away through the rainwater drain. On the other hand, icing of the drain hole will allow P1 to increase and cause a lowering of the EPR indication. Greater exposure to a type of aircraft and listening to crew members who may be more familiar with it should indicate what to expect.

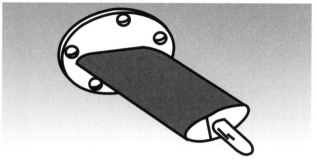

Figure 14-1. Ice detection probe.

It is essential to provide protection against icing of the engine and the leading edges of the air intake. An aircraft ice warning system can be simple and very effective, yet for some unknown reason, not all aircraft are provided with this useful item. [Figure 14-1]

Without proper ice warning, crews must resort to all manners of "homespun" methods for deciding when to apply engine heat for anti-icing. Some loss of engine thrust is associated with using anti-icing for the power plant. Therefore, the tendency is to not apply engine heating until it is obviously necessary.

Icing on engine intakes, or within the engine, can create airflow disturbances, causing a loss of engine performance and possibly a malfunction. A real threat with axial flow engines is that ice breaking away will be ingested, and result in damage to both the engine and its acoustic linings. For this reason, heating of axial flow engines needs to be considered as anti-, not de-, icing. [Figure 14-2]

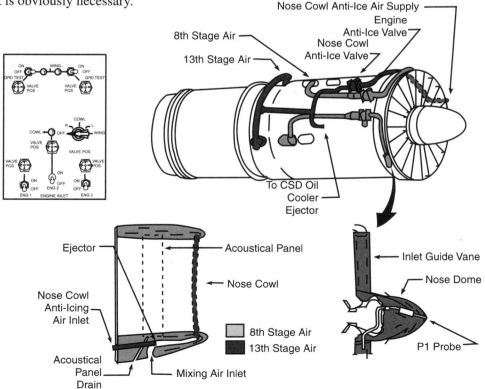

Figure 14-2. Turbine engine anti-ice.

Paradoxically, centrifugal compressors thrive on a little ice ingestion, and have been known to show an increase in thrust after ice passes into the engine. Dust and dirt particles bake onto the surface of the impeller when operating, and slowly lower its efficiency. Ice passing into the engine scuffs the impeller clean.

An effective engine anti-ice system must reliably cope with all possible icing conditions within the aircraft's operating envelope. The system must cause the least possible loss of engine performance, be easy to maintain, and not introduce a severe weight penalty. Even with jet aircraft speeds, it is common to take precautions against ice for an hour or more when on cruise.

In the design office, analyses are carried out to determine if, and to what extent, anti-icing will be required on the engine. Should difficulties arise, test rigs may be used to spray water onto engine intakes in the test house and/or in flight.

One or both of the following anti- and de-icing methods will be used on a gas turbine engine:

1.   Jet and fan engines use hot air that is bled from the compressor.

2.   Turboprops need electric heating for propeller blades, and therefore, may have all-electric or a combined thermal-and-electric means of combating engine ice.

THERMAL ANTI-ICING

Protection against ice buildup is only provided where it is needed. Axial compressor rotor blades are not likely to need anti-ice protection because of centrifugal

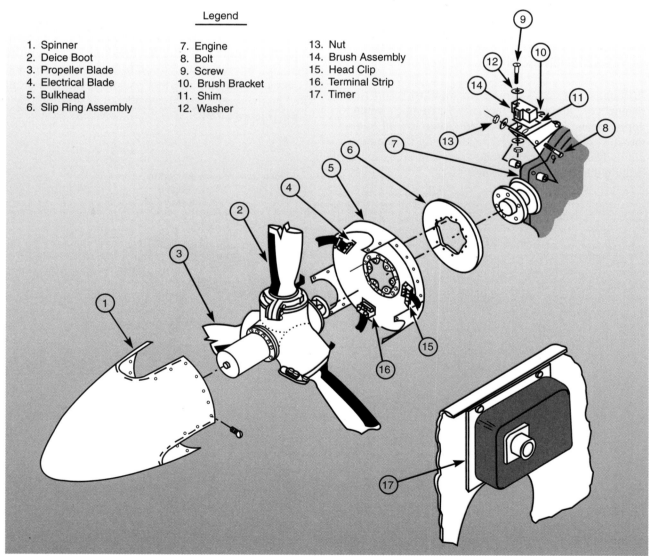

Legend

1. Spinner	7. Engine	13. Nut
2. Deice Boot	8. Bolt	14. Brush Assembly
3. Propeller Blade	9. Screw	15. Head Clip
4. Electrical Blade	10. Brush Bracket	16. Terminal Strip
5. Bulkhead	11. Shim	17. Timer
6. Slip Ring Assembly	12. Washer	

Figure 14-3. Propeller electrical de-icing system.

forces. Ice accretion on rotor blades is considered a low risk. Stator vanes located before the first stage of the compressor rotor blades may require heating. The rotating nose cone may not require heating, but it is usually given a continuous flow of hot air when taking anti-ice precautions.

In most applications, hot air for anti-icing is taken from the high-pressure compressor by controllable air bleed valves, then passed by pressure-regulating valves to anti-ice ducts, and onward to those parts of the engine to be anti-iced.

Spent hot air from anti-icing the nose cowl is vented into the compressor intake or overboard. Pressure-regulating valves in anti-ice systems are powered electrically in response to either manual selection from the cockpit, or to automatic selection from the aircraft ice detector. As the name implies, pressure-regulating valves prevent excessive pressures downstream of themselves. They also serve to limit the amount of air bled from the engine at high power settings, as on take-off.

In the event of a known anti-ice valve malfunction it may be acceptable, on multi-engine machines, to lock the valve either open or closed before take-off. Such action must be strictly in accordance with conditions set down in the minimum equipment list (MEL); a schedule of items of aircraft equipment which may be unserviceable for further flight. Performance-wise, it will be of special interest to check if weight penalties will apply to flight with bleed valves locked open.

ELECTRICAL DE- AND ANTI-ICING

Because turboprops require electrical operation of propeller blade anti-icing, it is common for them to apply electrical means to the intake cowl, and in some cases, the oil cooling air intake. Electrical heating strip conductors are sandwiched between layers of fiberglass or neoprene, then bonded onto cowl leading edges. A final coat of polyurethane paint protects the conductors against rain and dust. With electrical heating methods, some areas are continually heated to prevent ice accretion, while others are heated intermittently to break away ice that has formed. [Figure 14-3]

For electric generators to be of a reasonable size, de-ice loads are cycled between the engine and the propeller. A typical sequence is shown in figure 14-4. High is for heavy icing, and low is for lighter icing.

Aircraft icing will not take place at very cold temperatures, such as in cirrus clouds, but heavy icing can

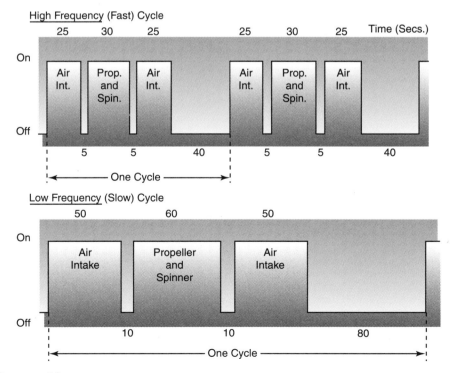

Figure 14-4. Turboprop anti-ice sequences.

occur on airframe and engine parts at Outside Air Temperatures (OATs) above or below zero degrees Celsius.

With the passage of time, and no doubt as the result of icing investigations, engine manufacturers and aircraft operators have become increasingly conservative in their attitudes toward icing. For example, the manufacturer of some well-proven aircraft advocates the use of engine heat for takeoff anytime that the OAT is less than +8° C, and visibility is less than one mile due to visible moisture such as rain, snow, sleet, drizzle, or fog.

Air that passes through the compressor, but does not contribute to thrust, is termed "internal air." At certain times, as much as 20% of mass airflow may be utilized for purposes other than thrust.

Bleed valves on engine compressors may be opened to supply convenient sources of energy to many services on modern aircraft. Typically, bleed air may be applied to:

1. Cabin air conditioning and pressurization.
2. Airframe thermal ice protection.
3. Engine thermal anti-icing.
4. Operation of thrust reversers.
5. Pre-cooling of heat exchangers.
6. Electric alternator cooling.
7. Cooling alternator Constant Speed Drive oil.
8. Fuel heating.
9. Hydraulic reservoir pressurization.
10. Blowing over cockpit windshields for rain removal.

In addition, cooling and sealing air is permanently tapped from the compressors whenever the engine is running. The quantity and the paths taken by this air are determined during engine design and are beyond the control of crew members. [Figure 15-1]

Since bleeding air from an engine lowers its thrust output, multi-engine aircraft incorporate a means of automatically closing the bleed valves of high demand services in an emergency. This feature is important during takeoff. Should an engine fail at a critical stage of flight, bleed valves automatically close on the power units still operating so that maximum thrust is available if it is required. Bleeding air from the earliest possible compressor stages minimizes performance losses.

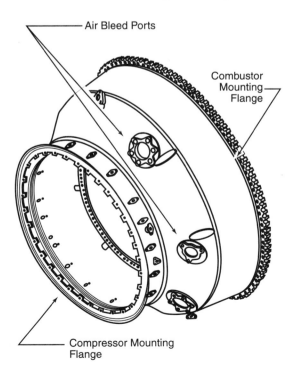

Figure 15-1. Air bleed ports.

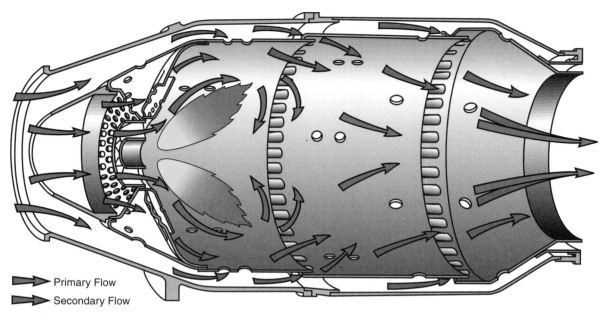

Primary Flow
Secondary Flow

Figure 15-2. Secondary cooling air.

COOLING

Cooling airflow inside the engine must be given consideration very early in the design process. Many components would suffer detrimental effects if subjected to the full possible heat transfer from hot sections. [Figure 15-2] The turbine and the combustor have the greatest need for cooling air.

As the temperature of an engine rises after starting, all its metal parts expand. Careful calculation ensures that this thermal growth does not alter the minimum clearances required by blade tips and seals. Care must be taken to see that the high temperatures required for efficiency do not exceed the limits of turbine blade and nozzle guide vane materials.

Interstage seals control the cooling airflow between turbine stages. The air is dumped into the main gas stream once its cooling function is achieved. For the most part, bearing chambers are maintained at a satisfactory temperature by engine lubricating oil. Having shaft bearings located in the cooler regions of the engine is an added precaution. If a bearing should require cooling air, a space between double-skinned housings will receive airflow.

Turbojet accessories, which are cooled in flight by atmospheric air, usually require some form of induced airflow cooling when on the ground. In this case, external air is induced to flow over the component by ejecting compressor air downstream of the cooling exit. This system may activate automatically from the clos-ing of an undercarriage leg switch on landing, or it may require manual selection. An air-scoop facing into the propeller wash supplies turboprop cooling air.

SEALING

Jet engine seals serve three purposes:

1. To prevent oil leaking from bearing chambers.

2. To control cooling airflow.

3. To provide an additional barrier in preventing combustion gases from passing through turbine disk cavities.

Several types of seal are available for GTE use. Factors in deciding which is most suitable include weight, wear resistance, seal heat generation, space available, plus ease of manufacture, installation, and removal.

Labyrinth Seals

Labyrinth seals are widely used and take many forms. [Figure 15-3] They allow control or metering of internal air-flows and retain lubricating oil in bearing chambers. Series of rotating circular blades or fins initially bear against an abradable lining in the static bore. Early in the life of the seal, the fins cut into the soft abrasive material to provide a minimum clearance between the fixed and rotating parts. The pressure drop across each fin is low so that only a restricted flow of sealing air takes place across the labyrinth. Airflow from outside to inside the bearing chamber prevents oil loss in the opposite direction.

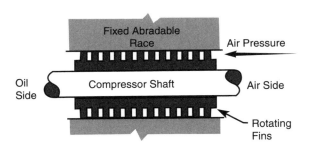

Figure 15-3. Labyrinth seal.

When in flight, an engine fault may cause a drop in oil pressure, and the engine must be shut down once a specified low pressure is reached. A very low oil pressure would allow the airflow to scavenge the bearing completely, resulting in a dry bearing.

A rotating annulus of oil could be used in place of the abrasive material if the shaft's flexing causes heat to be generated by excess abrasion.

Ring Seals

A ring seal is provided by a groove in the static housing holding a close-fitting metal ring. This ring is free to rotate when making contact with the rapidly turning shaft. Such seals are used for bearing chamber sealing, except in the hot areas where hot lubricating oil could cause seizure of the ring in its housing.

Hydraulic Seals

A hydraulic seal is formed by a fin tip penetrating the surface of an oil annulus; the latter is formed by centrifugal force. Unlike the labyrinth and ring seals, the hydraulic seal allows no controlled airflow across it. Compensation for differences in air pressure inside and outside the bearing chamber results in oil level differences on each side of the fin.

Brush Seals

A rotating shaft carries a collar of hard ceramic material. Rings of fine wire bristles attached to the static housing bear against this collar. The brush seal so formed produces a non-leaking component that copes well with the rubbing from flexing shafts. These seals may be encountered in older engines.

Carbon Seals

A static ring of carbon segments, held in place by springs, rubs continuously against a rotating shaft collar. The high degree of contact prevents oil or air loss, and the engine's circulating oil carries frictional heat away.

Chapter 16

Fire

Gas turbine engines incorporate features that lower the risk of fire. These features include fire prevention, fire detection and warning systems, and fire extinguishing systems.

ACTION IN THE EVENT OF FIRE

Each aircraft has a published checklist of actions to take in emergencies, including a specific one for engine fire. The checklist should be adhered to, but it is essential to remember that to stop a fire, the supply of combustibles must be stopped. That is, it is necessary to cut off the supply of fuel at the tank or as close to that as possible.

Even without fuel supply, an engine in flight will continue to rotate by windmilling, and engine oil will continue to circulate. This should not present a risk of continuing a fire because:

1. With fuel supply cut at the tank, an engine fire should burn itself out in a short time. The engine will then rapidly cool below a temperature at which combustion can take place.

2. Most oil transfer passages are internal.

3. Although the oil pump turns, pressure will be low.

4. The quantity of oil is relatively low.

Discharge of the fire-fighting bottles is done at the pilot's discretion. Most aircraft carry only two bottles of fire extinguishing agent. It is normal to discharge the first bottle immediately, as called for by the checklist, then wait at least 30 seconds to assess the results before deciding if the second bottle should be discharged. [See figure 16-1 on the next page.]

For ground operations and before commencing flight, it is always essential to have a full quota of fire-fighting equipment.

PREVENTION OF FIRE

Engines are designed to prevent the occurrence of a fire as much as possible. Mostly, some form of double failure is required to start an engine fire.

Potential fire sources are located away from the "hot end." If possible, fuel and oil components are placed in the "cool zone" near the compressor. A fireproof bulkhead of steel or titanium is built between the cool zone and the turbine/tailpipe hot zone. All zones are lightly ventilated to prevent pockets of flammable vapors from accumulating. Such buildups are further guarded against by having adequate drainage, such as liquid seals that drain overboard.

Piping for fuel, lubricating oil, and hydraulic oil is fireproof or fire resistant. Some engines utilize double-walled tubing if any combustibles must be carried through hot zones. In case of inner tubing failure, the outer tubing will carry the full flow and prevent leakage.

Engine pods and surroundings are cooled and ventilated by atmospheric air, not bleed air, passing around the engine then being dumped. While airflow around the engine must be sufficient to purge flammable vapor buildups, it must not be too high. High airflow would present unnecessary drag and would require excessive amounts of extinguishing agent should a fire erupt. Limiting airflow around the engine also ensures that any fire's intensity is low. Air pressure buildup within a cowl will be lowered when a preset pressure relief door opens; when the pressure is released, the door closes again.

Pressure differentials between hot and cold zones reduce the possibility of a fire spreading.

High Mach number aircraft use a blast of cooling air around an engine to prevent spontaneous combustion. This may have to be shut off in case of an engine fire to allow the extinguishing agent to obtain a sufficient concentration to be effective.

FIRE DETECTION

It is necessary to detect a fire rapidly, and there should be no false alarms. The problem of false alarms in aircraft is great because false alarms of any sort (fire, ground proximity, door warning lights, instrument failure, etc.) lead to crew uncertainty. False fire alarms or a complete loss of a detector system is possible from chafing, moisture, or a loss of gas pressure, depending on the detector method used.

A fire detection system may consist of a series of well-located individual detector units or a continuous ele-

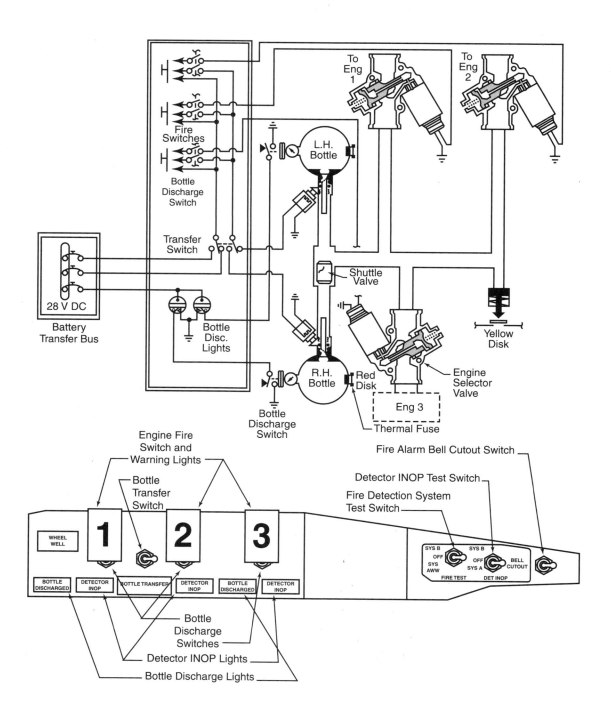

Figure 16-1. Boeing 727 fire extinguishing system.

ment (gas filled or electric) sensing type. It has been found very effective to place detector elements across ventilation outlets to provide an early warning of a fire.

Electric fire detectors respond to the changing electrical characteristics associated with temperature variations. Three types are in common use:

1. Thermistor

2. Thermocouple

3. Continuous electrical element

In each of the above, a temperature increase creates a signal that, after amplification, operates the warning indicator. Thermocouples and thermistor detectors are both well suited to this task. The thermistor is a semiconductor device with a resistance that decreases rapidly with increasing temperature. A thermocouple exposed to a temperature increase at its hot junction produces an EMF, which triggers the warning device.

In a thermistor, the constantly applied current varies in response to a variation of resistance as the temperature rises. This triggers the warning. A thermistor may be a single point detector or a continuous element type.

Another continuous element detector is the capacitance type. It is formed by a tube that contains a dielectric material, and a conducting wire runs the full length in the tube's center. A voltage difference is applied between the center wire and the tube wall. As the temperature increases, properties of the dielectric material change with equivalent changes in the unit's capacitance. The change in capacitance initiates a fire warning signal. [Figure 16-2]

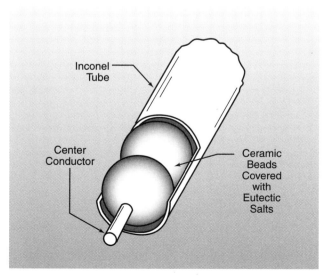

Figure 16-2. Capacitance-type (Fenwal continuous-loop) system.

A gas-filled type of detector is a stainless steel tube holding a material which readily absorbs the gas. As the temperature of a section of tube rises, gas is released from the material, increasing pressure within the tube. A rapid increase of pressure is sensed, and an appropriate warning is initiated. A fault in the detector loop that allows gas to escape from the tube is indicated on a cockpit warning unit. [Figure 16-3]

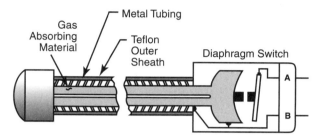

Figure 16-3. Gas-filled-type (Lindberg pneumatic continuous-loop) system.

Cockpit fire warning methods may be visual, aural, or tactile. Sometimes a combination of two or all three is used. A fire warning is always a loud, distinct ringing bell. The bell is not used for any warning except fire. In addition, one or more red lights will be prominently displayed to show the location of the fire. It is normal to test all fire warning systems before engine start on each flight.

Although an engine fire can spread to other parts of the aircraft, an engine is designed so that a fire due to some fault will be contained within the engine. Aluminum cowls are not in themselves fireproof, but in-flight airflow makes them satisfactory for fire containment. In addition to being used for firewalls, steel and titanium are employed in areas exposed to any possible flame.

FIRE EXTINGUISHING

An engine on fire must be shut down before releasing extinguishing agent. By design, items such as start lever linkages, lubricating oil and hydraulic shut-off valves, and generator cooling blast shut-off must be located outside the hot zone to prevent possible malfunction due to fire damage.

Halon compounds are used as extinguishing agents, although some older aircraft may be supplied with CO_2. The extinguishing agent is held in metal bottles under pressure, and is located in areas outside of fire risk.

Manual activation of an electric circuit fires a small cartridge at the bottle's discharge head. Extinguishing agent flows via supply tubes and is sprayed onto the selected area by nozzles or perforated spray pipes. At least two shots of extinguishing agent are supplied per aircraft, not per engine. The discharged extinguishing agent must reach and maintain specified concentrations for periods of 0.5 to 2 seconds. [Figure 16-4]

Unless an extreme emergency subsequently arises, there must be no attempt to restart an engine that is shut down due to fire. If attempting to restart an engine that is shut down due to fire, it is probable that it will start burning again and there may not be any more extinguishing agent available.

ENGINE OVERHEAT

In the short term, overheating of a turbine does not introduce a serious immediate risk of fire. However, if overheating is permitted to continue, it could bring about turbine disintegration and fire could follow. In any case, to prevent damage, early detection of engine overheating is essential to allow shut down.

A warning system for excessive temperatures is used that is similar to fire detection systems. Again, having detectors in cooling air outlets has proven to be effective in warning of engine overheating.

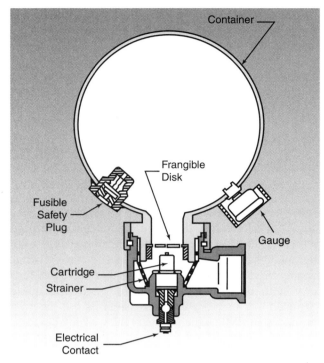

Figure 16-4. Fire extinguisher bottle.

Chapter 17

Water/Methanol

As the maximum output of a gas turbine engine (GTE) varies with the density (mass) of the airflow through it, a reduction of thrust or shaft horsepower (SHP) will result as the density of air decreases. Air density decreases with an increase in altitude, or with an increase of ambient air temperature.

On a hot day, an airfield at sea level may have a "density altitude" of several thousand feet. This means that thrust available from an engine at sea level will be as low as that at a higher altitude—the "density altitude." Important aircraft performance factors such as maximum weight, takeoff distance required, accelerate-stop distance, performance speeds, and in multi-engine aircraft, the climb-out gradient available after failure of a power unit, will all be affected. Restoring thrust to sea level values is desirable. This is achieved by cooling air to increase mass flow through the engine. The cooling is achieved by a spray of water or a water/methanol mix. This process is often referred to as "water injection." It provides the mass increase, and is capable of boosting thrust above normal maximum values when demanded.

Cooling liquid is introduced to the engine at two locations: sometimes at the combustion chamber inlet, sometimes at the engine air intake; and sometimes both simultaneously. For simplicity, the two individual cases are considered separately, and Figure 17-1 applies to the combined arrangement.

COMBUSTION CHAMBER INJECTION
The principle of injecting coolant into the combustion chamber inlet is most often applied to axial flow engines. Injecting coolant increases mass flow through the turbine relative to that through the compressor. Pressure- and temperature-drops across the turbine are thereby reduced, and jet pipe pressure and thrust increase above the non-cooled values.

When combustion chamber coolant is water-only, there is a reduction of turbine entry temperature (TET). Compensation is provided by an increase in fuel flow. If a methanol component is present in a coolant mix, that component will combust to regain turbine entry temperature without fuel flow adjustment. The methanol acts as a non-conventional fuel which also has anti-freeze qualities.

COMPRESSOR INLET INJECTION
Compressor inlet injection of coolant is typically applied to turboprop intake air. When the system is switched on, coolant flows from the aircraft tank to a servo controlled metering valve. Extent of valve opening is in response to propeller shaft torque and ambient air pressure, thus, appropriate thrust augmentation is applied. Combustion of the methanol component has similar effects to those mentioned above.

A large drop in torque, as with a multi-engine aircraft having engine failure on takeoff, can initiate auto-feather functioning.

Obviously, all applicable normal engine limitations must be observed in routine operations. Indicator lights, one for each engine, will illuminate in the cockpit when the coolant flows into the engines.

A word of warning is appropriate when dealing with water injection: only use the correct water/methanol mixture specified for the particular engine. Some time ago, a medium-sized passenger jet in northern Europe had its water/methanol tank filled with aviation kerosene by mistake. On the subsequent takeoff, shortly after becoming airborne, both engines overheated, then failed completely. All on board were lost.

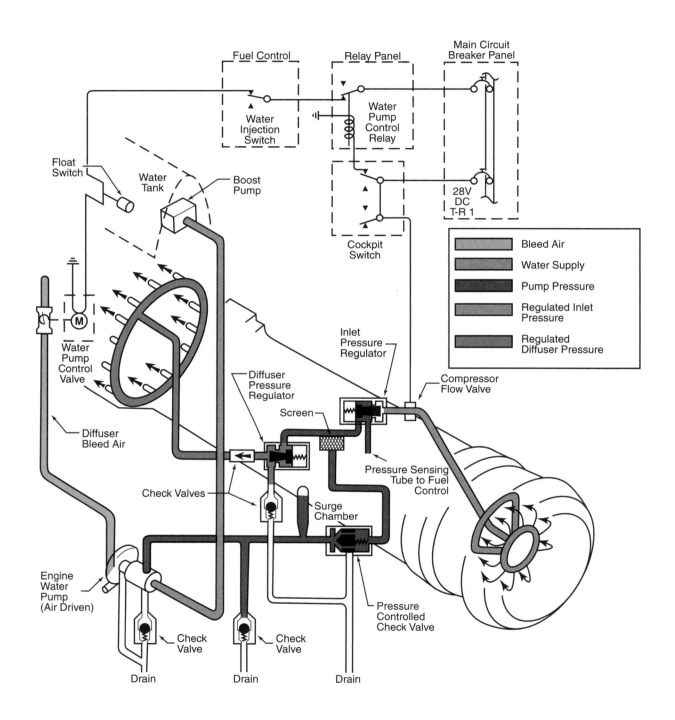

Figure 17-1. Water injection system.

Chapter 18

Instruments

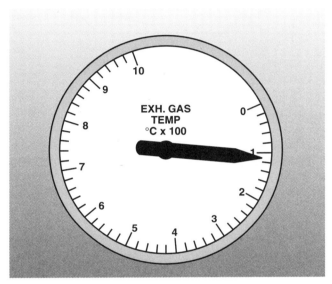

Figure 18-1. Exhaust gas temperature (EGT) gauge.

Multi-engine aircraft have flight instruments immediately in front of each pilot. Between flight panels is a centrally located panel of major engine instruments. Aircraft fitted with the so-called "glass cockpits" have a cathode ray tube (CRT) or liquid crystal flat plate presentation, upon which the required instrument images may be brought up on demand. The screen is located in a similarly centralized position between the flight instrument displays.

EXHAUST GAS TEMPERATURE

The most important engine parameter to be monitored by the flight crew is the exhaust gas temperature (EGT). For emphasis, it is restated that what is really being monitored is the temperature at the point of entry to the turbine, the turbine entry temperature (TET), which may be known as the Turbine Inlet Temperature (TIT). For applications in the aircraft itself, it is impracticable to measure TET due to construction complications. By having thermocouples in the tailpipe gas stream, the crew is given temperature information that relates directly to the upstream temperature at the turbine. With accurate control of EGT, the crew ensures correct TET. In some locations EGT may be referred to as jet pipe temperature (JPT). [Figure 18-1]

Half a dozen or more thermocouples are placed inside the tailpipe circumference, projecting into the gas stream. [Figure 18-2] Connecting the thermocouples in parallel electric circuits provides an average temperature and permits continued use of the system even if several thermocouples fail. Holes in the probe container tubes provide a quicker response to the temperature indicating system. The holes allow hot gases to flow directly onto the thermocouple hot junctions. Additional functions may be carried out by increasing the number of circuits connected to the probes. For example, a signal can be supplied to the engine maximum temperature control system.

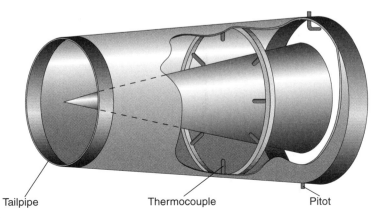

Tailpipe   Thermocouple   Pitot

Figure 18-2. Tailpipe.

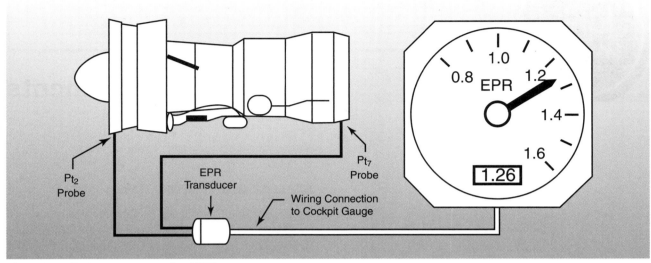

Figure 18-3. Engine pressure reading (EPR) gauge.

In the test cell, it is possible to use a radiation pyrometer to measure the radiated energy from the turbine blades, and convert that into a temperature indication. The pyrometer is located in the turbine nozzle case with the lens system focused directly onto the turbine blades. Readings from the pyrometer are amplified and used to indicate temperature on a large test-house dial.

ENGINE THRUST

Engine-developed thrust is indicated to the flight crew in one of two ways:

1. The first indicates turbine discharge or tailpipe pressure as it is received by one or more pitots facing into the gas stream. This method is not a popular one.

2. The second makes use of similar pitots in the gas stream to assess the pressure at engine station 7 (P7). Another line supplies the pitot pressure at engine station 1 (P1) at the inlet to the compressor. Installations may vary; in some, P1 is supplied from a central inlet in the nose bullet; in others, it is taken at engine station 2, as in Figure 18-3. In either case, P1=P2.

The ratio of P7/P1 is the engine pressure ratio (EPR). Being a ratio, EPR is a simple number, such as 1.95, 2.10, etc., is quite sensitive and gives a good appreciation of engine thrust for practical use. A fan engine may derive EPR by integrating the values of the fan outlet and engine discharge pressures. For convenience, EPR pitot head readings are averaged in a fashion similar to that of thermocouple averaging. [Figure 18-3]

ENGINE R.P.M.

GTEs always have some indication of r.p.m. In a two-spool engine, N_1 and N_2 rotational speeds are indicated, while a three-spool engine often includes an intermediate speed indication.

The most common system makes use of a small three-phase electrical alternator. When turned by the engine the alternator produces a current, the frequency of which is proportional to engine r.p.m. With electro-

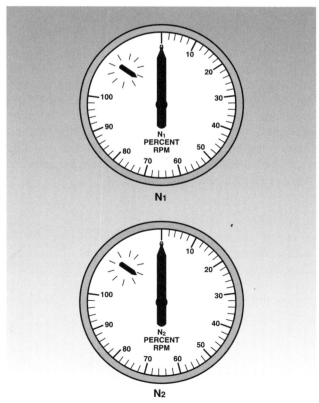

Figure 18-4. Tachometers.

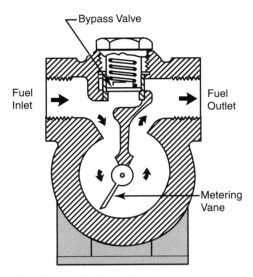

Figure 18-5. Electric flow transmitter.

mechanical indicating systems, a synchronous motor in the cockpit indicator moves in response to alternator frequency. [Figure 18-4]

OIL PRESSURE AND TEMPERATURE

Oil pressure and temperature indications are provided for each engine in an aircraft. These indications are essential to correctly operate a gas turbine. These systems are similar to those used in reciprocating engines. In most, a low-pressure light warns that continuing to operate that engine could result in damage. As pointed out in Chapter 15, operating with the light on can produce bearing failures.

FUEL FLOW

Attractiveness of an aircraft is always affected by its range; the further it can go, the greater the attractiveness. This means that more fuel must be squeezed into shapes determined by other factors. Larger aircraft have many fuel cells making up one tank. Pilots are concerned about total fuel quantities and do not need information on individual cells. Even with the most modern equipment, determining the amount of fuel that remains in each tank is not always precise. By commencing a flight with known quantities of fuel, and deducting the amounts that have passed through fuel flow measuring devices, it is possible to obtain figures for the fuel that remains, and make the best decisions for conducting the following flight stages. Fuel flow (F/F) indications are accurate and reliable.

An electric flow transmitter is in the fuel low-pressure supply line. Its readings are transmitted to an indicator in the cockpit. Of simple construction, an electric flow transmitter is, in effect, a vane that is displaced as flow rates increase. Vane positions are sent to the cockpit

and registered as flow rates. Some F/F cockpit indicators include a digital totalizer showing the total pounds or kilograms consumed. They are reset to zero before startup of each flight. [Figure 18-5]

Weights play such an important part in daily aircraft operations that it is customary to refer to fuel in terms of pounds or kilograms. Very little reference is made to fuel volumes.

VIBRATION

Because the GTE has such smooth, almost vibration-free functioning, any small vibration increase may pass unnoticed. However, a small vibration increase could occur before a major engine malfunction. As a precaution, pick-offs are located at several points on the engine to monitor vibration changes. Any particular engine will have its own acceptable vibration level, which will be noted. An increase in the vibration should be treated as a warning for a possible failure in the future.

Some aircraft vibration indicators are connected to the master warning system. This guarantees that any vibration beyond definite limits is brought to the attention of the operating crew.

FUEL PRESSURE AND TEMPERATURE

Only the fuel low-pressure system will have these indications of pressure and temperature. Although not always fitted on an airplane, they are helpful in monitoring the overall functioning of the engine. In some airplanes, a fuel low-pressure filter is fitted with a differential pressure switch. Some filters warn of partial filter blockage by operating a light that warns of possible fuel starvation. Complete reliance on such automatic warning devices is unwise. With full instrumentation, crew members can monitor all happenings.

ENGINE TORQUE

To indicate power developed by a turboprop, engine torque is measured at the reduction gear and shown on the instrument known as the "torque meter." The

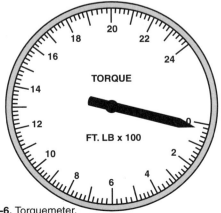

Figure 18-6. Torquemeter.

engine's turning moment, its torque, is proportional to the horsepower developed and transmitted to the propeller shaft. Axial thrust in the reduction gears is opposed by oil pressure acting on a number of pistons provided for this purpose. [Figure 18-6]

Oil pressure is measured and presented on the cockpit instrument in p.s.i. In addition to supplying a cockpit indication of engine power, the torque meter system may provide two more services:

1. It may be used to initiate propeller auto-feathering on takeoff if torque pressure falls due to engine failure.

2. It may be used to initiate water injection supply to the engine on normal takeoffs.

SYNCHRONIZING

Even with rear-mounted engines, it is possible for the cockpit crew to hear the audible "beat" from single-spool engines when they are not correctly synchronized. A multi-engine turboprop will produce a similar beat from unsynchronized propellers. The uninitiated may regard this beating as minor, but if it continues for hours, it can be irritating and tiring when these slight differences in r.p.m. exist between engines. One solution to the problem is to have special engine-mounted electric generators which produce signals that vary with engine r.p.m. These signals vary fuel flow from the fuel control unit and effectively trim the engines to match r.p.m.

Conventional cockpit r.p.m. indicators are not sufficiently accurate for synchronizing. Automatic synchronizers usually work quite well but it may be necessary to manually compensate a slave propeller or turbine rotor. Manual fine trimming may be done by deactivating the automatic synchronizer and manually adjusting the r.p.m. by use of a special cockpit presentation. Single-spool turbojets may be synchronized in such a manner, while multi-spool engines can only have one spool synchronized in each slave engine.

ELECTRONIC DISPLAYS

Cockpits that utilize electronic indicating systems provide big improvements in the monitoring of engine and aircraft systems. One such incorporates the Electronic Indicating and Crew Alerting System (EICAS) for crew

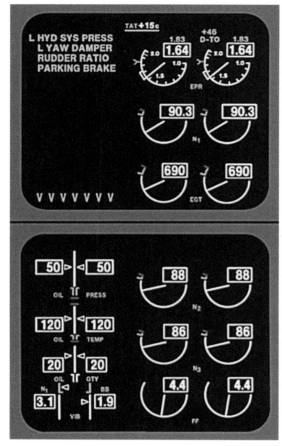

Figure 18-7. Electronic indicating system.

information. Similar systems may have differing aconyms and functions. In any of these systems, a pilot has a wide selection of parameters for display on screens. In the EICAS case, warnings and associated alerts are presented in written words on the screens. These days information from triple inertial navigation systems (INS), integrated with spatial location details from double global navigation systems (GNS), combine with EICAS-type readings to provide a high level of current information to crews. Applicable information detail is stored in computers for later analysis on completion of a flight. [Figure 18-7]

Nevertheless, total reliance on automatic systems is ill advised. To be worthy of the title "pilot," a person should be able to control the airplane and its engines at all times. To be computer savvy is desirable. However, true pilots need to retain use of the computer that sits between their ears.

Chapter 19

Accessory Drives

At first glance, the components of a GTE appear randomly placed. However, the essential accessories and associated gearboxes are carefully positioned. Also, most components are specifically designed for a particular engine, and the power required for any given component's operation is clearly known. Stresses produced in drive shafts and gear trains can be accurately calculated in order to apply safety margins. Accessories are attached directly to the faced pads of gearbox housings, and are grouped around the cold section of the engine for fire safety reasons.

The N_2 assembly in a multi-spool engine is the one cranked for starting. Therefore, it is logical to drive the engine's accessories from that assembly.

The N_2 shaft has a beveled gear wheel that engages another beveled gear. This drives one or a series of minor shafts that transmit power to external gearboxes. [Figure 19-1]

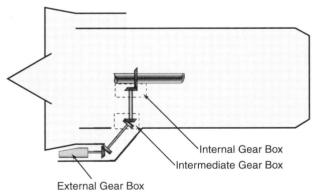

Figure 19-1. Accessory drive principle.

Sometimes, a low speed gearbox that is limited to light duties will be driven by the N_1 shaft, which only rotates on start as a result of N_2 airflow through the engine. [Figure 19-2]

A gear train provides yet another method for powering gearboxes. There is little of consequence between the shaft or gear train drives. [Figure 19-3]

An interesting special case is that of the constant speed drive (CSD), which is standard on many multi-engine

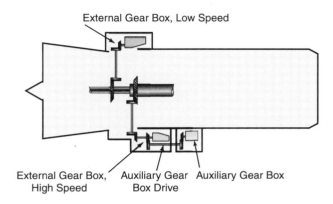

Figure 19-2. N_1 accessory drive.

aircraft. For many years, multi-engine aircraft were obliged to utilize DC as their primary electric supply, while inverters supplied AC to special units. It was often stated that aircraft could never use AC, despite its advantages, because of the practical difficulties in phase synchronizing the alternators for parallel feeding to a common bus bar.

Much of the electrical equipment functions at particular voltages and frequencies. Alternators fitted to engines need to rotate at a constant speed, even though engine speeds must vary according to aircraft requirements. A CSD placed between the engine and the alternator makes this possible. A CSD is a form of electrically or mechanically controlled hydraulic transmission.

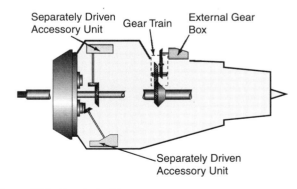

Figure 19-3. Gear train drive.

If the engine r.p.m. is between 2,800 and 9,000, then the alternator r.p.m. will be fixed at 6,000. With engine r.p.m. below 6,000, the CSD steps up its output to maintain 6,000 r.p.m. to the alternator. If engine r.p.m. exceeds 6,000, the CSD steps down its output to maintain 6,000 r.p.m. to the alternator. By properly synchronizing, several alternators may feed one common AC bus.

The CSD is dependent upon a self-contained amount of oil for its hydraulic drive, and it has electric circuits monitoring its oil quantity. If the oil quantity falls below a definite limit, a warning light illuminates in the cockpit and the CSD drive must be disconnected.

Chapter 20

Performance

The operating envelope of an engine is decided by the manner in which it is to be used. Military and various commercial applications call for differing specifications.

Turbojet performance is measured in terms of thrust available at the propelling nozzle. Turboprop performance is measured in shaft horsepower (SHP), which is provided to the propeller at the propeller shaft; i.e. after the reduction gear has reduced the propeller shaft r.p.m. In each case, the assessment of thrust, or SHP, for comparisons between the engines is that developed for a given weight, frontal area, or fuel consumption.

Developed thrust or SHP depend upon:

1. The mass of air entering the engine.

2. Acceleration given to the air in the engine.

These two factors are influenced by:

(a) Aircraft forward speed.

(b) Aircraft altitude.

(c) Atmospheric conditions.

Of these three variables, aircraft forward speed is influenced by:

- Air intake efficiency.

- Compressor efficiency.

- Combustor efficiency.

- Turbine efficiency.

- Exhaust efficiency.

These efficiencies are influenced by (a), (b), and (c).

Figure 20-1 illustrates these interactions that affect the amount of energy extracted from the gas stream to provide jet thrust or shaft horsepower.

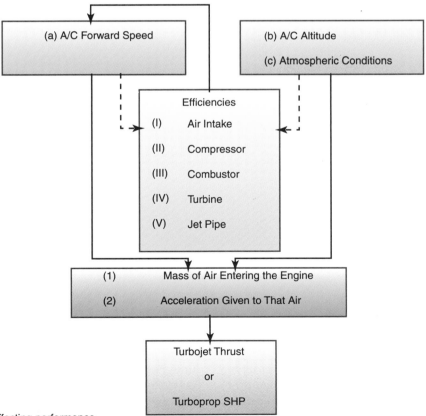

Figure 20-1. Factors affecting performance.

Sections of the engine may have gas velocities as high as 2,500 ft/sec or more, however, the local Mach number stays below 1.0 because of the high gas temperatures.

To obtain the maximum number of miles from any particular quantity of fuel, the thrust, or SHP, needs to be maximized while the rate of fuel consumption is minimized. Known as the specific fuel consumption (SFC), this factor is expressed in pounds of fuel per hour per pound of thrust, or per SHP (lb. fuel/hr/lb. thrust, or lb. fuel/hr/SHP). The achieved SFC is controlled by the engine's thermal and propulsive efficiencies.

Thermal efficiency is often known as "internal efficiency," and propulsive efficiency as "external efficiency." For a given energy output of an engine, thermal and propulsive efficiencies have a large influence on compressor and turbine sizes.

STATIC AND FLIGHT THRUSTS

Engine performance figures are reduced to standard atmosphere values to allow similar engines to be compared at different geographical locations. Several standard atmospheres have been defined. The most commonly used is the international standard atmosphere (ISA) in which the following apply:

- ISA temperatures at mean sea level (MSL) = 15° C with a lapse rate of 2° per thousand feet of altitude increase up to 36,000 ft. Thereafter, the temperature is considered constant up to an altitude of 66,000 ft. To be precise, the temperature lapse rate is 1.98° C per thousand feet of altitude increase (2° C is normally accepted).

- ISA MSL pressure is 1013.2 hPa (hectopascals) = 29.92 inches Hg.

We shall first consider the unchoked engine. Let the velocity of the gas at the jet be V_j, the velocity of the aircraft be V, and the weight of air passing through the engine be W lb./sec. The mass of air passing through per second is W/g, and the acceleration (a) of the air = $V_j - V$.

Under test bed (engine static) conditions, V is zero. Thrust is the product of the mass of transiting air and the velocity at the propelling nozzle; i.e. thrust = $M \times V_j = M \times a$.

When airborne, thrust is the product of the mass of air going through the engine per second times the difference of the jet exit velocity minus the forward speed of the aircraft; i.e. thrust = $M \times (V_j - V) = M \times a$.

Restating for clarity:

Formula (1)   thrust on the bench = $W/g \times (V_j - 0)$ = $M \times V_j$

Formula (2)   thrust in flight = $W/g \times (V_j - V)$

So far, concerning an unchoked nozzle, only the energy due to velocity has been considered. The next step addresses the effect of using a choked nozzle because additional thrust (pressure thrust) that results from residual pressure is present. The choked nozzle provides additional thrust as a result of its static (non-kinetic) pressure (being higher than atmospheric pressure) acting over the cross sectional area of the propelling nozzle.

If:

A = the propelling nozzle area in square inches

P = the static (non-kinetic) gas pressure at the nozzle (psi)

Po = atmospheric pressure (psi)

Then the effective pressure acting across the nozzle = $P - P_o$, and the additional thrust = pressure × area = $(P - P_o) \times A$.

So when a choked nozzle is used:

Formula (3)   total test bench thrust = $(P - P_o) \times A + W/g \times V_j$

Formula (4)   airborne thrust = $(P - P_o) \times A + W/g \times (V_j - V)$

All formulae, (1), (2), (3), and (4), show that thrust may be increased by increasing the mass of air that passes through the engine and by increasing the jet velocity.

An engine's output may be given a short-term boost in one of two ways:

1. By increasing mass flow, as when using water injection

2. By increasing jet velocity using afterburning

Air density changes mean air mass changes for GTE applications. Therefore, measured thrust is influenced by changes in atmospheric air pressure and temperature. Numerical calculation of thrust variations produced by air density changes does not concern pilots. However, pilots must be alert to engine performance changes that result from these effects.

TURBOPROP THRUST

A turboprop will always have some amount of jet thrust that must be added to its SHP to determine the engine's total output. The additional amount added to SHP is known as thrust horsepower (THP). Total equivalent horsepower (TEHP) is the sum of SHP and the SHP equivalent coming from residual jet thrust (TEHP = SHP + THP).

For calculation purposes, it is taken that one SHP = 2.6 lb. of jet thrust under ISA MSL static conditions. Therefore, for turboprops: TEHP = SHP + pounds of jet thrust / 2.6.

Many factors affect the proportions of SHP and jet thrust. A turboprop will usually provide about 1 lb. of jet thrust for each 3.5 to 5 SHP that it produces.

MOMENTUM DRAG

Unchoked flight thrust can be arrived at by a slightly different path. "Momentum drag," or "intake drag" as it is sometimes known, is drag due to the momentum change of atmospheric air passing into the engine at aircraft velocity V. Therefore, momentum drag is given by $W/g \times V$, where W/g equals the mass of air passing through per second.

To obtain the force propelling the aircraft (net thrust), momentum drag must be taken into consideration and deducted from gross thrust.

NET THRUST = GROSS THRUST - MOMENTUM DRAG

$= \quad W/g \times Vj - W/g \times V$

$= \quad W/g (Vj - V)$

$= \quad M \times a$ (which is the same expression previously developed for thrust in flight in the unchoked case, as in formula (2).)

In the choked nozzle, gross thrust requires the addition of pressure thrust, i.e. gross thrust $= (P - Po) \times A + W/g \times Vj$.

NET THRUST $= (P - Po) \times A + W/g \times Vj - W/g \times V$

$= \quad (P - Po) \times A + W/g (Vj - V)$ (which is the same as formula (4).)

Momentum drag is considered negligible during take-off so gross and net thrusts are taken as equal.

AFTERBURN CONSIDERATIONS

When an engine is static and afterburn is turned on, an increase in thrust of at least 30% is experienced by a pure jet, and much more with a bypass engine. Due to ram effect under flight conditions, the increase in thrust from afterburning is still greater. Momentum drag remains the same at a given speed with or without afterburn, but by using afterburn, better utilization is made of each pound of air that goes through the engine. The following arithmetic example illustrates this improvement:

> Assuming an aircraft speed of 520 kt (845 ft/sec), each pound of air going through the engine produces a momentum drag of $1 \times 845/32 = 26.4$ lb.

In other words, for every pound of air going into the engine per second, and being accelerated up to aircraft speed, a drag of 26.4 lb. results. Assuming a gross thrust of 75.0 lb. is produced by every pound of transiting air each second, the net thrust (gross thrust - momentum drag) will be 75.0 - 26.4 = 48.6 lb. If afterburn is now selected on while maintaining 520 kt, gross thrust becomes $1.3 \times 75 = 97.5$ lb./lb. air/sec.; and net thrust = 97.5 - 26.4 = 71.1 lb./lb. air/sec.

Therefore, the ratio of net thrust with and without afterburn at 520 kt is 71.1/48.6 = 1.46. Expressed differently, a 30% increase of thrust from afterburn on the ground becomes a 46% increase in net thrust when airborne at 520 kt.

The actual thrust obtained by using afterburn is limited by both the amount of unused oxygen remaining in the gas stream, and the gas temperature at the afterburner itself. With no previous combustion taking place in the duct, bypass engines are well suited to the application of afterburn. Static thrust increases of 70% or more are achievable with bypass engines. When airborne at high speeds, increases in net thrust will be several times greater than this figure.

Specific and total fuel consumptions increase dramatically when using afterburn. However, the penalties are not considered excessive in view of the large increases in aircraft performance.

RAM RATIO EFFECTS

Ram ratio is defined as the ratio of total air pressure at the compressor entry to the engine intake's static air pressure (P1/Po). It may be noted in passing that similar pressures are used to obtain airspeed readings in the cockpit. However, whereas the ASI uses a difference of pressures, the application in this instance concerns pressure ratios. The in-flight choked thrust Formula 4 $[(P - Po) + W/g (Vj - V)]$ shows that if jet velocity remains constant, independent of aircraft speed, then net thrust decreases as the aircraft gains speed.

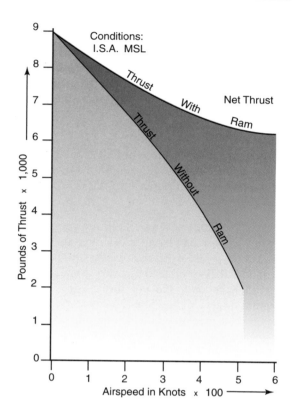

Figure 20-2. Ram ratio effects at MSL.

Due to the ram ratio effect from the forward speed of the aircraft (i.e. from extra air being taken into the engine), the mass airflow and the jet exit velocity both increase with aircraft forward speed. (With more air entering the engine, the jet exhaust speed must increase; otherwise, the engine would inflate like a balloon.) The overall tendency is for the ram ratio effect to offset the extra momentum drag resulting from airspeed increase. The final result is that net thrust partially recovers as speed increases. [Figure 20-2]

At trans- and supersonic speeds, drag rise caused by shock waves from air intakes could, if neglected, destroy any ram ratio gains. Unless suitably designed air intake shapes are adopted, the ram pressure rise will fall away rapidly. Also, ram air temperature rises rapidly at supersonic speeds, thereby increasing the compressor delivery temperature. To maintain thrust, the engine would require higher turbine entry temperatures (TET), but these are limited by turbine assembly materials. These considerations add considerably to the design difficulties of engines operating at high speeds.

EFFECTS OF AIRSPEED CHANGES

The increase of mass airflow that comes from increases in aircraft speed must be matched by a fuel flow

increase if r.p.m. is to be maintained. This causes an increase in fuel consumed. As net thrust tends to decrease with increasing airspeed, the SFC rises. [Figure 20-3]

High aircraft speeds at low levels would produce great engine stresses, if permitted to happen, because of ram ratio effect. Fuel flow is automatically reduced to prevent overstressing of the engine at low levels. Engine speed and airflow remain within limits.

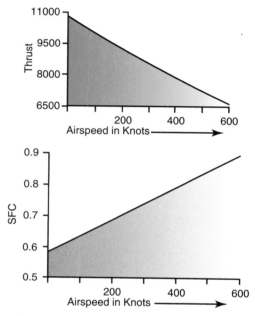

Figure 20-3. Increasing airspeed affecting thrust and SFC.

EFFECTS OF ALTITUDE CHANGES

Increasing altitude reduces the ambient air pressure and temperature, and the engine is affected in two interrelated ways:

1. Lowering pressure when gaining altitude reduces air density and, therefore, mass airflow to the engine at any given r.p.m. Reducing mass airflow causes engine thrust, or SHP, to decrease. In order to maintain constant r.p.m. during a climb, the fuel control unit (FCU) adjusts the fuel pump output to match the mass airflow.

2. Air temperature decreases with a gain in altitude, thus tending to increase the air's density. This factor considered alone would increase the mass airflow for constant r.p.m.

The combined effects of 1 and 2 cause mass airflow to decline as the altitude increases, but at a lower rate than

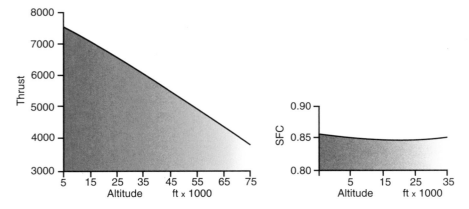

Figure 20-4. Altitude influences on thrust and SFC.

if the pressure change was the only factor. Because of the lowering temperature, there is partial compensation for the thrust loss which would come from pressure reductions alone. As aircraft altitudes increase, decreases of both temperature and pressure result in continuous reductions of thrust, with only a small change in SFC. [Figure 20-4]

EFFECTS OF TEMPERATURE CHANGES

On a cold day, air entering the compressor is more dense than would be the case on an ISA day; the mass of air entering the engine at any given r.p.m. is increased, thus thrust or SHP would increase. However, denser air requires higher power to drive the compressor, and the engine will require more fuel to maintain r.p.m. Alternatively, if there is no increase of fuel, r.p.m. will decrease.

Fuel is supplied to the engine by the fuel control unit (FCU) in such a way that, at low temperatures, the maximum amount of fuel supplied is almost constant. Engine r.p.m. decrease slightly, but the thrust lost is counterbalanced by the thrust gained from mass rise. The result is almost no change in net thrust when air that is colder than ISA values is present.

Although low-pressure spool speed (N_1) is routinely less than high-pressure spool speed (N_2), the difference between the speeds is reduced as temperatures drop below ISA.

Under normal conditions, varying the fuel flow in response to N_2 r.p.m. automatically controls the entire engine r.p.m. To prevent any tendency for N_1 to overspeed, an additional governor, known as the N_1 governor, is fitted to the low-pressure spool; it reduces total fuel supply when necessary.

When surface temperature falls below a predetermined value, a "pressure ratio" fuel system will schedule the amount of combustion fuel to maintain a constant EPR and, therefore, constant thrust. If the outside air temperature (OAT) is above the datum, then some engines automatically control the fuel flow to prevent turbine gas temperature (TGT) from being exceeded. Other engines require the throttle to be retarded slightly as the exhaust gas temperature (EGT) limit is approached.

It is interesting to know that an engine may experience a thrust loss at takeoff as great as 20% when ambient air temperature reaches 45° C. For this reason, some form of thrust augmentation, such as water injection or afterburn, may be desirable for takeoff when conditions are much above ISA.

EFFICIENCIES

GTE performance is judged not only by the thrust it produces, but also by the efficiency with which it converts fuel heat energy into kinetic energy, and how it utilizes the latter to drive the aircraft forward. Thermal efficiency and propulsive efficiency are both considered.

For best thermal efficiency, combustion product temperature must be as high as possible. However, the temperature limit imposed by the guide vane/turbine environment must not be exceeded. The efficiency with which kinetic energy is converted to propulsion is the propulsive efficiency.

Kinetic energy dissipated in the jet wake is a loss, and is expressed as $1/2\ W/g \times v$ (i.e. KE = $1/2\ W/g \times v$) where (v) = waste energy, and is proportional to the previously defined Vj - V. Although the jet continues to issue from the engine at an unchanged Vj, its difference of velocity relative to the surrounding air is reduced at higher aircraft speed V. Hence, the lower the aircraft's forward speed, the higher the jet waste of energy (v).

For a jet aircraft, the waste is most significant at the lower end of its speed range, where a propeller's efficiency is greater. As aircraft speed increases, this factor changes in favor of the turbojet. [Figure 20-5]

Propulsive efficiency may be calculated by using the simplified expression $2V / (V + V_j)$. This simplification may be applied to both choked and non-choked nozzles. In the choked case, V_j is the jet velocity when the jet has fully expanded to atmospheric pressure. Some figures may give greater appreciation.

Assuming an aircraft speed of 340 kt and a jet velocity of 1120 kt, the propulsive efficiency will be $2 \times 340 / (340 + 1120) = 680/1460 = 47\%$ at 340 kt. For the same turbojet at 515 kt, the propulsive efficiency $= 2 \times 515 / (515 + 1120) = 1030/1635 = 63\%$. The propulsive efficiency increases from 47% to 63% due to the speed increase of the aircraft.

Although a turboprop could not be operated at such high speeds, a calculation of projected propeller efficiencies at speeds of 340 and 515 kt would be approximately 80% and 59%, respectively. Figure 20-5 shows that aircraft operating at less than about 400 kt achieve

their best propulsive efficiency of GTEs by gearing to a propeller.

At higher airspeeds, propeller efficiency decreases rapidly due to shock waves at blade tips as their speed approaches M 1.0.

By applying the bypass principle, airframes suited to commercial operation may obtain good propulsive efficiency without the complexities of gearing to a propeller system. The bypass engine bridges the efficiency gap between turboprop and pure jet. A typical triple-spool high-bypass engine will have a propulsive efficiency in the order of 85% at an aircraft speed of M 0.8.

High bypass ratios of 5:1 and beyond, applied to triple-spool designs, provide the desired pressure and bypass ratios with short compressor rotors and fewer stages. Engines of reduced length and bulk are the result.

Low SFC and low engine weight are of prime importance in designing engines for commercial transports. Continual improvements in engines are made through applications of the bypass principle, advanced aerody-

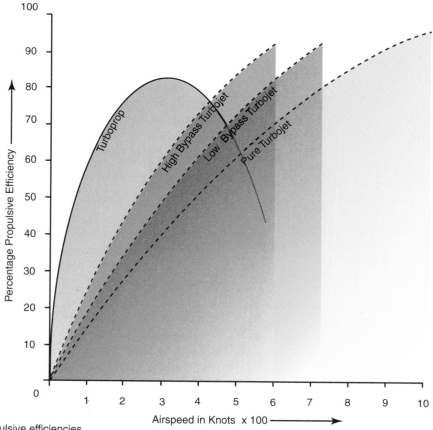

Figure 20-5. Propulsive efficiencies.

namic and mechanical features, and through improved materials.

Although pure theory requires only a high pressure ratio to reach high thermal efficiency, in practice, high TETs are also required because of inefficiencies in the compression and expansion processes. In a pure jet, this necessary high temperature raises jet velocity to reduce propulsive efficiency. Bypassing a portion of the LP compressor air reduces the jet temperature and velocity, thereby improving thermal and propulsive efficiencies, and giving good SFCs.

Pure jets require heavy (strong) turbines because they process the total airflow passing through the engines. This contrasts with bypass engines in which the turbines work on only a part of the total airflow. As a result, high-pressure compressors, combustion chambers, and turbines can be reduced in size.

To take full advantage of the capacity of its turbine, the bypass engine uses high values of pressure ratio and TET. These are acceptable to the turbine because reducing its diameter lowers centrifugal stresses at any particular r.p.m..

For any given thrust, the bypass engine is lighter than its pure jet counterpart. This is for two reasons:

1. The diameter of the high-pressure N_2 assemblies if reduced.

2. The length of the engine is reduced.

For a given mass airflow, the bypass engine will be about 20% lighter than a pure jet, even if the bypass ratio is quite low.

Good design of triple-spool high-bypass engines significantly reduces the number of parts needed. Rotating assemblies are better matched, and therefore operate at closer to their optima. These factors, plus the use of high-strength, low-weight materials, produce efficient engines with low SFCs.

A minor drawback of the bypass engine is that, for any given mass airflow, it produces less pounds of thrust than does a pure jet. This is because the bypass engine has the lower jet exit velocity. For a bypass engine to provide the same thrust as a pure jet engine, its size would need to be increased somewhat, in order to process an increased airflow. Despite this small handicap, the weight of the bypass engine will still be lower than that of the pure jet because of the smaller HP section. Compared with a pure jet engine, the bypass type shows an improved power/weight ratio.

Chapter 21

Calculating Thrust

Engine principles should be understood by now, although thrust distribution inside the engine may be unclear.

To establish the forces acting in each section of a GTE, we assume it to be static, single-spool, and choked. The forces present are due to the pressure and momentum changes in the gas stream acting upon the engine components. The forces are considered positive if they provide thrust and negative if they oppose it. The difference between the total positive (+ve) and negative (-ve) forces produces what we refer to as the engine's static thrust. [Figure 21-1]

If mass flow, pressures, areas, and velocities are known for the inlet and outlet of engine sections, then thrust forces can be calculated for each by considering the existing differences between the inlet and the outlet.

Although the true value of "g," the gravitational constant, is 32.2 ft./sec./sec., it is acceptable to use 32 ft./sec./sec. to simplify the arithmetic. Calculations are done using gauge pressure, not absolute pressure. In this way, MSL air pressure is zero. The formula is:
THRUST = $A \times P + W/g \times V_j$ where:

A	= flow section area in square inches.
P	= pressure in psi.
W/g	= mass airflow in lb./sec.
V_j	= outlet velocity.

COMPRESSOR

As the first step, it is necessary to calculate the conditions at the compressor inlet and outlet. Because static conditions have been assumed, pressure and velocity at the inlet are zero. Calculations only need to be made for the outlet.

Given:	Outlet area	A = 177 sq. in.
	Outlet pressure	P = 89 psi.

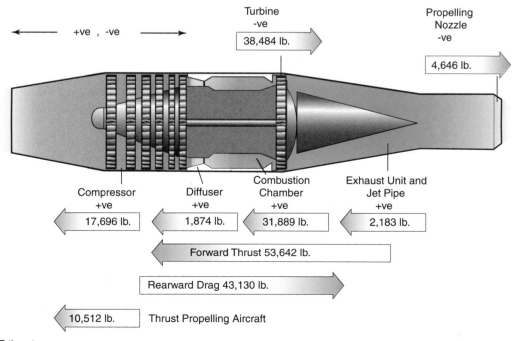

Figure 21-1. GTE thrust.

Outlet velocity   Vj = 423 ft./sec.

Outlet mass flow   W/g = 147/32 lb./sec.

Compressor thrust = the difference between A × P + W/g × Vj and zero: 177 × 89 + 147/32 × 423 = 17,696 lb. +ve. Create a table of two columns; one labeled +ve for positive and one labeled -ve for negative. Enter the figure 17,696 in a table under +ve.

DIFFUSER

Diffuser inlet value is the same as compressor outlet: 17,696 lb.

Given: Outlet area   A = 198 sq. in.

              Outlet pressure   P = 90 psi.

              Outlet velocity   Vj = 381 ft./sec.

              Outlet mass flow   W/g = 147/32 lb./sec.

Diffuser outlet thrust = 198 × 90 + 147/32 × 381 = 19,570 lb.

Thrust across the diffuser = the difference between the outlet and inlet thrust: 19,570 - 17,696 = 1,874 lb. +ve. Enter 1,874 in the table under +ve.

COMBUSTOR

Given: Outlet area   A = 568 sq. in.

              Outlet pressure   P = 88 psi.

              Outlet velocity   Vj = 321 ft./sec.

              Outlet mass flow   W/g = 147/32 lb./sec.

Combustor outlet thrust = 568 × 88 + 147/32 × 321 = 51,459 lb.

Thrust across the combustor = the difference between the outlet and inlet thrust: 51,459 - 19,570 = 31,889 lb. +ve. Enter 31,889 in the table under +ve.

TURBINE

Given: Outlet area   A = 466 sq. in.

              Outlet pressure   P = 19 psi.

              Outlet velocity   Vj = 897 ft./sec.

              Outlet mass flow   W/g = 147/32 lb./sec.

Turbine outlet thrust = 466 × 19 + 147/32 × 897 = 12,975 lb.

Thrust across the turbine = the difference between the outlet and inlet thrust: 12,975 - 51,459 = -38,484 -ve. Enter 38,484 in the table under -ve.

EXHAUST AND JET PIPE

Given: Outlet area   A = 638 sq. in.

              Outlet pressure   P = 19 psi.

              Outlet velocity   Vj = 661 ft./sec.

              Outlet mass flow   W/g = 147/32 lb./sec.

Exhaust and jet pipe outlet thrust = 638 × 19 + 147/32 × 661 = 15,158 lb.

Thrust across the exhaust and jet pipe = the difference between the outlet and inlet thrusts: 15,158 - 12,975 = 2,183 lb. +ve. Enter 2,183 in the table under +ve.

PROPELLING NOZZLE

Given: Outlet area   A = 319 sq. in.

              Outlet pressure   P = 5 psi.

              Outlet velocity   Vj = 1941 ft./sec.

              Outlet mass flow   W/g = 147/32 lb./sec.

Propelling nozzle outlet thrust = 319 × 5 + 147/32 × 1941 = 10,512 lb.

Thrust across the propelling nozzle = the difference between the outlet and inlet thrust: 10,512 - 15,158 = -4,646 -ve. Enter 4,646 in the table under -ve.

The table is now:

+ve	-ve
17,696	38,484
1,874	4,646
31,889	- -
2,183	- -
53,642	43,130

Therefore, the engine thrust is the difference between total +ve and -ve values; i.e. 53,642 - 43,130 = 10,512 lb. by summing the component thrusts.

Now to compare the thrust just found with the calculation of the engine thrust as a whole unit. From Formula 3 in Chapter 20, the expression for thrust of the choked engine is THRUST = (P - Po) × A + W/g (Vj - 0) when static. Using gauge pressures, Po is zero. Thus, the thrust for the engine is (5 - 0) × 319 + 147/32 × (1941 - 0) = 1,595 + 8,917 = 10,512 lb. as before.

THRUST VS. POWER

Probably the most commonly asked question concerning the GTE is, "How much power does it produce?" The answer is not very straightforward. If you were to lean on Cheops' Pyramid and push with all your

Figure 21-2. If the pyramid doesn't move, no work is performed.

strength for as long as you were able, you would do no work in the scientific sense even though you were becoming quite tired. By definition, work is force × distance. For you to have done work, you should have moved the object to which you applied force. It is reasonable to assume that the Pyramid would not have moved. Further, power is the rate of doing work. Therefore, if no work, then no power! [Figure 21-2]

Now, consider two airplanes standing at the takeoff points of their runways, one a propeller aircraft, and the other a jet. [Figure 21-3] If both were to hold on the brakes while their throttles were opened fully, the situation would be:

1. The engine of the propeller aircraft would be delivering maximum power to the propeller via the propeller shaft.

2. Because it is stationary, the engine of the jet aircraft would be doing no work despite being at maximum static thrust. As in the case of Cheops' Pyramid, no work, no power.

To make comparisons, speed must be considered; then a value can be given to the jet in terms of thrust horsepower (THP).

Power is force (lb.) × velocity (ft./sec.) foot pounds per second, and 1 HP is 550 ft.lb./sec.

So, THP = force (lb.) × velocity (ft./sec.) / 550. THP = F × V/550

By substituting aircraft speed in ft./sec. for V, and thrust in lb. for F, the THP can be calculated.

Also, 325 kt = 375 m.p.h. = 550 ft./sec. So, at 325 kt, a thrust of 1 pound would produce a THP of 1 × 550 / 550 = 1. Expressed differently, 1 lb. of thrust = 1 THP at 325 kt.

A ratio of speeds can be used to obtain THP at other airspeeds. For example, if a turbojet produces 8000 lb. of thrust at an airspeed of 500 kt, the THP at that speed is 8000 × 500/325 = 12,308 THP. Interesting, but of little practical importance.

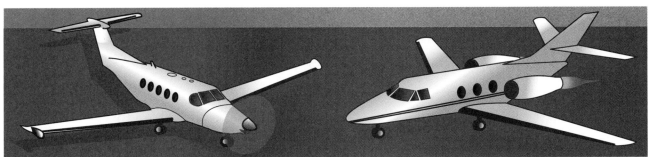

Figure 21-3. The turboprop is doing work since the prop is turning. The jet is not doing any work since it is not moving.

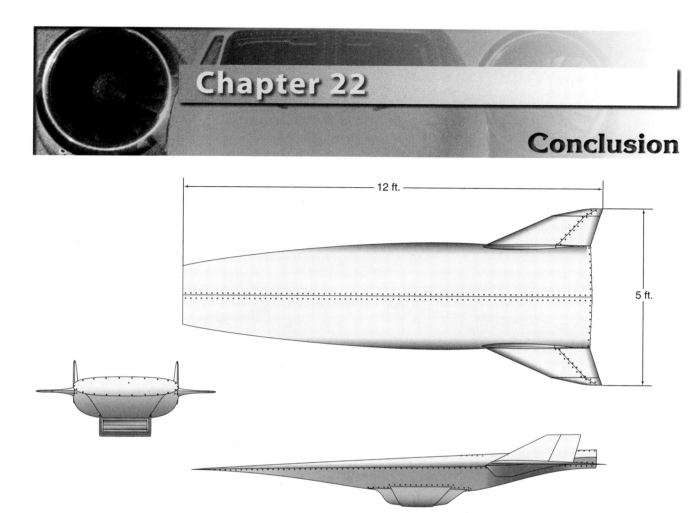

Figure 22-1. The NASA X43a will use scram jet engines to reach M 10.0 in the atmosphere.

Looking into the future is the domain of novelists and fortunetellers. Attempting to anticipate any future developments in aviation propulsion would be difficult and probably inaccurate.

Each engine of the original Meteors provided 1,700 lb. of thrust. Each of the four engines of later B 707s and DC 8s provided about 16,000 lb. of thrust. Currently, single engines are producing more than one-and-a-half times the total thrust of those four-engine aircraft. Commercial interests will be paramount in determining where the thrust growth will stop. Paying passengers have yet to decide if two-engine aircraft offer the same degree of safety as do three- and four-engine types.

A range of possible developments is being examined in research laboratories where small engines are being operated beyond M 4.0. Forward thinking extends into the realm of M 25.0! Presently being investigated is something known as a "Scram Jet," which incorporates supersonic combustion. Engineers are experimenting with exotic fuels and even injecting hydrogen into kerosene fuel. For transport in the earth's atmosphere, the attainable high speeds would be attractive. [Figure 22-1]

An attractive possibility is the pulse-detonated engine (PDE). A recent proposition that is now being developed, the PDE is a thrust-producing engine that has no moving parts. Essentially an open-ended tube with a carefully designed intake, it operates at several thousand cycles per second. Much lighter than a GTE of similar thrust, and with fuel consumption lowered by 30%, its advantages are obvious. A PDE is capable of functioning from nil forward speed to Mach 3 or beyond. In some respects, it may be likened to the German V1 engine of 1944 (Chapter 1, pg. 1-2). Near the front end of the tube, a combustible fuel/air mixture is ignited and the detonation wave travels at a very high speed toward the exit. The tube's pressure forward of the shock wave decreases to induce further fuel for the subsequent cycle repetition. The PDE has the environ-

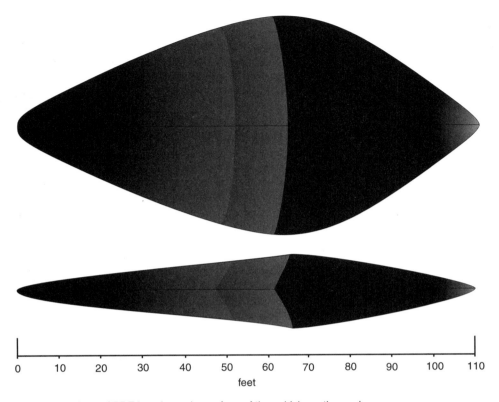

Figure 22-2. One possible form of PDE has the entire surface of the vehicle as the engine.

mental disadvantage of burning fossil fuel, while its noise levels have yet to be determined. [Figure 22-2]

Vehicles in space are using ion engines to accelerate minute masses and are capable of non-stop operation for a year or more. Experiments are being made with laser power beamed from earth. No doubt, security considerations are responsible for hiding many advanced concepts from the public.

It has been forecast that, by the year 2050, responsible governments will have banned flight at cruise altitudes favored by today's commercial aircraft, because of the long-term cumulative increase in CO_2 deposited by jet exhausts at those flight levels. With human population numbers increasing, and vast areas of forest which convert carbon dioxide into oxygen being destroyed every year, eventually mankind will be forced to face problems resulting from carbon fuel combustion. Burning carbon fuel produces accelerations of gas turbine engine gases. The engine would function satisfactorily without combustion, as we know it, if heat could be added to the air; perhaps by nuclear fusion if that ever becomes a reality. Should this come about, we shall have progressed right back to the basics of Mr. Stolze's patent of 1872.

APU	auxiliary power unit	EC	European Community
AC	alternating current	EGT	exhaust gas temperature
Athodyd	aerothermodynamic duct	EMF	electromotive force (voltage)
AUL	Approved Unserviceable List		
AVGAS	aviation gasoline	FCU	fuel control unit
AVTUR	aviation turbine fuel	F/F	fuel flow
a	acceleration	FL	flight level
		FOB	fuel on board
Buckets	reverser components	FOD	foreign object damage
		FSN	fuel spray nozzle
C	Celsius (centigrade) temperature	ft/sec	feet per second
CD	convergent-divergent duct (venturi)	fps	foot/pound/second system
Clamshells	reverser components		
Corrugated Nozzle	noise reducing component	gal	gallon
CO	carbon monoxide	GFP	ground fine pitch
CO_2	carbon dioxide	GTE	gas turbine engine
CRT	cathode ray tube		
CSD	constant speed drive	HE	high energy
		Hg	inches of mercury (pressure)
DC	direct current	HP	horsepower
DC	divergent-convergent duct	HP	high pressure
DME	distance measuring equipment	hr	hour

IAS	indicated air speed	P	pressure
ISA	international standard atmosphere	P1	pressure at station 1 (engine nose)
		P7	tailpipe pressure
j	joule (energy unit)	Pitot	French engineer 1695 - 1771
JPT	jet pipe temperature	PRV	pressure relief valve
		psi	pounds per square inch
kt	knot (1 nm/hr)	PV	pressure-volume (diagram)
KE	kinetic energy		
		RAF	Royal Air Force
lb	pound	r.p.m.	revolutions per minute
Lobe nozzle	noise reducing component		
LP	low pressure		
Luftwaffe	German air force	sec	second (time)
		SFC	specific fuel consumption
		SG	specific gravity
M	Mach	SHP	shaft horsepower
MEL	minimum equipment list	Spool	compressor/shaft/turbine assembly
m.p.h.	miles per hour		
MSL	mean sea level		
		T	thrust
N	rotational speed, r.p.m.	T	temperature (absolute)
N_1	low-pressure spool	TEHP	thrust equivalent horsepower
N_2	high-pressure spool	TET	turbine entry temperature
NATO	North Atlantic Treaty Organization	TGT	turbine gas temperature
nm	nautical mile	THP	thrust horsepower
N_2O	nitrous oxide	Translating cowl	thrust reverser component
OAT	outside air temperature		
O	oxygen	UV	ultraviolet

V   volume

V1   pulse jet powered flying bomb

V2   liquid fuel rocket

w/m   water/methanol coolant mix

Formula (1) engine unchoked, static:
$$T = W/g \times Vj$$

Formula (2) engine unchoked, flight:
$$T = W/g \times (Vj - V)$$

Formula (3) engine choked, static:
$$T = (P - Po) \times A + W/g \times Vj$$

Formula (4) engine choked, flight:
$$T = (P - Po) \times A + W/g \times (Vj - V)$$

+ve   positive

-ve   negative

$\propto$ is proportional to

%   percent

Appendix B

Mach Table

Mach 1.0 @   15 C = 661 kt = 1115 ft/sec

Mach 1.0 @ 500 C = 1083 kt = 1827 ft/sec

Mach 1.0 @   800 C = 1305 kt = 2200 ft/sec

Mach 1.0 @ 1000 C = 1390 kt = 2346 ft/sec

Mach 1.0 @ 1200 C = 1495 kt = 2520 ft/sec

Mach 1.0 @ 1500 C = 1640 kt = 2769 ft/sec

Mach 1.0 @ 2000 C = 1857 kt = 3135 ft/sec

Index

DISCOVER YOUR FUTURE!

FULL COLOR TEXT. FULL IMPACT LEARNING.

Jeppesen's Guided Flight Discovery Private Pilot Manual is an integral component within the GFD Pilot Training System. The organization and colorful presentation of the text helps students learn quickly from the start. Discovery insets expand on important ideas and concepts in the text. The information ties in references from the world of aviation, including NTSB investigations and aviation history. Human Element insets introduce pilots to the human factors aspect of flight.

ITEM NUMBER JS314500 PRIVATE PILOT MANUAL (INCLUDES FAR/AIM CD) $65.95
ITEM NUMBER JS314505 PRIVATE PILOT MANUAL (INCLUDES CD AND FAR/AIM TEXT) $72.95

GFD INSTRUMENT/COMMERCIAL MANUAL

Jeppesen's Guided Flight Discovery Instrument/Commercial Manual provides the most complete explanations of aeronautical concepts for professional pilots through the use of colorful illustrations and full-color photos. This primary source for initial study and review includes Principles of Instrument Flight, The Flight Environment, Instrument Charts and Procedures, Aviation Weather and IFR Flight Operations and Commercial Pilot Operations, as well as an introductory look at Building Professional Experience. The most comprehensive and visually appealing Instrument/Commercial Manual ever!

JS314520 INSTRUMENT/COMMERCIAL MANUAL $73.95
JS314525 INSTRUMENT/COMMERCIAL MANUAL WITH FAR/AIM TEXT $79.95

GFD Instrument/Commercial Syllabus Package
This training syllabus covers the learning objectives and time allocations for both Instrument Rating and Commercial Certificate. The syllabus also contains an option for a Multi-Engine Rating. In addition to the syllabus, this package also contains enrollment notices.
ITEM NUMBER JS344525 $14.95

GFD FLIGHT INSTRUCTOR MANUAL

Prepares CFI applicants for Flight Instructor-Airplane Certificate, Instrument-Airplane and Multi-Engine-Airplane Instructor Ratings. This 560-page, full-color text includes over 1,000 photos and illustrations in attractive GFD style. Workbook exercises, instructor endorsements, and a comprehensive glossary and index are included.

ITEM NUMBER JS314530 $69.00

AVIATION HISTORY BY JEPPESEN

Announcing one of the most significant books on aviation history that has been published to date. Aviation History is an exciting new full-color book that gives both new and experienced pilots a unique perspective on international aviation history. Each of the ten chapters is packed with information, containing over 950 photographs and color graphics. Aviation History explores the question "what was aviation" from its birth in Annonay, France, in 1783, to the exhilarating accomplishments in space. Through personal profiles, you are able to meet the people who made significant contributions to aviation. You will explore historical evidence and see how historians use the artifacts of aviation to confirm what happened. 636 pages.
ITEM NUMBER JS319008 $69.95

Aviation History Instructors Guide on Diskette *(Available for Flight Schools and Professors Only)*
ITEM NUMBER JS285321 $29.95

VISIT YOUR JEPPESEN DEALER OR CALL 1-800-621-5377
MAKE SURE TO CHECK OUT OUR WEB PAGE AT HTTP://WWW.JEPPESEN.COM
PRICES SUBJECT TO CHANGE.

Maintenance Training

Aviation Maintenance Training Publications In Complete Kit Form

Jeppesen's General, Airframe and Powerplant training materials come in complete kit form. Comprehensive, developed by respected experts in the field, these kits give students the information they need to succeed in obtaining their Airframe and Powerplant license. Student technicians around the world depend on the training material produced at Jeppesen. You'll find quality material in every publication produced by seasoned instructors and authors. Whether your a veteran, building your own plane, or just learning you can count on Jeppesen to help you get where you want to go. Jeppesen Maintenance products help you master the topic and realize success!

AIRFRAME

Airframe Kit
Includes the following: A&P Technician Airframe Textbook • A&P Technician Airframe Workbook • A&P Technician Airframe Study Guide • Student Kit Bag.
ITEM NUMBER JS302128 $54.95
KIT ITEMS ARE ALSO SOLD SEPARATELY

GENERAL

General Kit
Includes the following: A&P Technician General Textbook • A&P Technician General Workbook • A&P Technician General Study Guide • Acceptable Methods, Techniques and Practices/Aircraft Alterations (AC43.13-1B/2A) • FAR Handbook for Aviation Maintenance Technicians • Student Kit Bag.
ITEM NUMBER JS302182 $81.95
KIT ITEMS ARE ALSO SOLD SEPARATELY

POWERPLANT

Powerplant Kit Includes the following: A&P Technician Powerplant Textbook • A&P Technician Powerplant Workbook • A&P Technician Powerplant Study Guide • Powerplant Exam Package • Student Kit Bag. ITEM NUMBER JS302184 $51.95 *KIT ITEMS ARE ALSO SOLD SEPARATELY*

FAR Handbook for Aviation Maintenance Technicians Updated annually to include all changes published by the FAA in the previous year. Revisions are denoted by a dashed vertical revision bar in the left margin. The handbook contains only those FARs which are pertinent to aviation maintenance: 1, 13, 21, 23, 27, 33, 34, 35, 39, 43, 45, 47, 65, 91, 119, 125, 135, 145, 147, 183 as well as applicable SFARs. Includes Advisory Circulars 20-62, 20-109, 21-12A, 39-7B, 43-9C, 43.9-1E and 65-11B. **As an added bonus, each book contains a copy of the FAA-G-8082-11, "Inspection Authorization Study Guide."**
ITEM NUMBER JS312616 $19.95